INTERIOR VIEW OF THE NEENAH HIGH SCHOOL ROOM.

KRUEGER & LACHMANN.

A Flouring Mill Concern That Does an Exceedingly Large Business.

The Krueger & Lachmann Milling Co., which was incorporated April 20, 1894, operate one of the most substantial industries in the city, and do a business extend-

EX-MAYOR E. J. LACHMANN.

ng throughout the New England States, s far south as Baltimore, Md., all over he Middle States, the bulk of their trade f course being in Wisconsin, Illinois and Michigan. The company does a general merchant milling business and handle large uantities of grain. Their mills have a apacity of about 300 barrels per day and heir grain storage elevator and two wareouses have a capacity of 40,000 bushels hey manufacture superior grades of flour heir principal brands being: "Gilt Edge," first patent; "Island City," patent; and Standard," straight. They also manuacture excellent qualities of rye flour, rye raham, wheat graham and other cereal ours, and guarantee all their goods to be e equal of any on earth. In fact, the ompany's products have an enviable reptation wherever sold, and one order also sures additional ones. The officers of e company are: A. H. F. Krueger, president; T. H. Krueger, vice-president and E Lachmann, secretary, treasurer and anager.

The old stone mill, occupied by the comany, is that which was built in 1868 by tridde & Krueger, the latter being now resident of the Krueger & Lachmann Milling Co.

GILBERT PAPER CO.

One of the Most Important Concerns in the Twin Cities.

In referring to the great paper mills of e twin cities, THE NEWS in no case in is issue enters into lengthly detail deil description of either plants or their roductions, preferring to deal generally of e importance of the institutions to the ommunity. These great manufacturing instries are valuable to the city in that ey give steady employment to large numers of people, whose wage account in the ggregate reaches an enormous figure anually; and as the money thus earned preeates every avenue of local trade, the inerest our people take in the success of each the large manufacturing establishments manifest.

The Gilbert Paper Co. is among the rgest and most important in the Fox iver Valley, their plant being one of the usiest and best equipped in this section. he business was established under its esent title in 1887, and from its incepon the product of these mills has stood it prominently in the trade. Wherever ... and in consequence the mpany is never at a loss for orders, eir output being to the fullest capacity the mills. They manufacture fine sized ts and envelope papers and bond and hographic papers of superior qualities. e officers of the company are: Wm. bert, president; A. M. Gilbert, treaser, and T. M. Gilbert, secretary. The bert family is one of the oldest and st influential in this section, and during these years among us have been extene and liberal employers of labor.

DEPENDABLE DRUGS.

Drug Concern That Does Credit to the City of Neenah.

hat the Wilde Drug Company comd of F. A. Wilde and F. A. Wilde, jr., h succeeded the firm of Wilde & Glea- October 1, is conducting an establisht equal in many respects to any of e in the metropolitan centers is appar-o those familiar with the trade, and it is feature, together with the fact that article in the house coming under the of drugs bears the unmistakable p of purity and reliability, that is atng such an exceptionally large pate. And it is to this fact also, that be attributed the decided confidence ublic places in the filling of prescripat Wilde's—they know the ingredire absolutely pure; they know the positive accuracy in compounding is obtained; they know the utmost courvill be extended; they know there is ig desirable or dependable in drugs, etary remedies, toilet articles, etc., what can be found at Wilde's, and is making special efforts to corner the market on the prescription business of Neenah, and unless the unexpected happens every medicine bottle in the homes in this city will soon bear the label of "Wilde." The company is in every sense deserving of the confidence reposed in them in this respect, as they have spared no expense to prepare for this particular and most important branch of their business.

In addition to retailing, they do a general jobbing business in pharmaceuticals, representing such well known houses as Parke, Davis & Co., Sharp & Dohme, the W. S. Merrell Chemical Co., and others. They are also headquarters for books, office supplies, and stationery.

Don't forget your next perscription. If you want the best and safest, take it to

Wilde's
DRUG STORE

OUR LIGHTING SYSTEM.

The Neenah and Menasha Gas and Electric Co's Excellent Service.

That the Twin Cities are fortunate in the matter of light is due to the general excellence of the system operated by the Neenah and Menasha Gas and Electic company, both in street lights and those in our homes and places of business. This is the only company of its kind in the two cities, and so long as they continue the present very satisfactory service at anywhere near the same cost there will be no room for competition.

The plant which is modern in every particular, was established about 20 years ago, and from the day the company began business it has met with success. George A. Davis the secretary and general manager of the concern, is one or Neenah's best known and most enterprising men, whose earnest desire is to give the people the very best service possible.

PROF. O. J. SCHUSTER.

Supervising Principal of the Neenah High School.

Prof. Schuster, who succeeded Prof. W. N. Parker, now assistant state superintendent of public schools, on the first of last January, as supervising principal of

PROF. O. J. SCHUSTER.

the Neenah high school, is a young man of the highest mental calibre, and even in so short a time as he has been among us has shown himself to be particularly well qualified for the important position he occupies. All that the Neenah High school lost in the promotion of so learned a man as his predecessor, has been gained in the selection of Prof. Schuster, as has been demonstrated by the very able work he has done since he assumed charge here.

Prof. Schuster is essentially a self made man. A native of Wisconsin, having been born and reared in the little town of Middleton, he prepared himself by home study principally in the common branches of education, and so closely did he apply himself that he passed a most creditable examination preparatory to entering the State University, from which he graduated with honors in 1886. He at once took up his life's work and began teaching at Lodi. Later he taught in the public schools of Oconomowoc and afterward at Dodgeville, and when he received the call to assume charge of the High school in this city he was deeply engrossed in graduate work at the State University, and would have graduated therefrom in the third degree within a few months.

The Professor is possessed of a charming personality and has made many steadfast admirers and friends since locating in Neenah. He is especially respected by the pupils ... speak of him in high terms, both as friend and instructor.

N. H. S. FOOTBALL TEAM AT PRACTICE.

GEO. L. McDERMOTT, M. D.

A Young Physician with a most Promising Future.

Doctor George L. McDermott, although a young man, has made a splendid record as a member of the medical profession during the two and a half years he has been practicing, having surrounded himself with an unusually large practice considering the length of time he has been in business. The Doctor was born in this city in 1871, and it was here he received his common school education, rounding out the same at one of the prominent commercial colleges of Milwaukee. He is a son of Daniel McDermott, who is now one of the oldest living settlers of the county. The Doctor studied medicine at Rush Medical College, Chicago, graduating ... time he returned home and at once began the practice of medicine. He has been City Physician for the past two years, a position he has filled to the most eminent satisfaction of all concerned. He is a close student in his profession, and contributes many articles on timely subjects to the medical journals of the country.

The Doctor has offices on Church St., opposite the postoffice, his residence being on Commercial St. Telephone No. 150.

Doctor McDermott was married in February last to Miss Eva Considine, a most charming and accomplished young lady of Chicago. Mrs. McDermott is a vocalist and instrumentalist of no mean pretention, and her paintings have been highly praised by the critics. The Doctor and his estimable wife occupy a pleasant home on South Commercial Street.

DR. S. A. BOWE.

For More than Forty Years a Practicing Veterinary Surgeon.

Dr. S. A. Bowe, who opened an office on South River street, third door east of Commercial street, this fall, has been a practicing veterinary for more than forty years, having graduated from the Columbia Veterinary College in 1857. For several years he practiced in Michigan, and in 1861 entered the civil war as a member of the 66th Illinois, the western sharpshooters, serving until discharged for total disability. He returned to his home in Michigan and followed his profession, removing to Wisconsin in 1879. He located at Oshkosh, where he still retains his home. Since opening an office in Neenah the Doctor has met with marked success. Dr. Bowe is a na-

C. H. BERGSTROM.

A Well-Known Business Man for More Than Twenty Years.

It was 'way back on the first day of February, 1878, C. H. Bergstrom purchased the business which had been established by his father John Bergstrom and began on his own account, and from that day to the present he has been most successful. He manufactures and deals in fine carriages and cutters and has an exceptionally large trade in harness, bicycles and agricultural implements, including the time-tried John Deere plows and the famous Planet Junior cultivators. Mr. Bergstrom also does a general repair business in all his lines, in which he gives the very best satisfaction, all his workmen being experts at their trade.

Mr. Bergstrom has been a resident of Neenah about thirty years, and has always been foremost in every move that would tend to promote the city's best interests.

E. F. WIECKERT.

A Thoroughly Equiped and Well Established Plaining Mill.

For many years E. F. Wieckert has been been connected with the planing mill business of this city, during all of which time he has enjoyed an unusually prosperous business. Mr. Wieckert's plant is one of the largest and most complete in this section and all his work is of the most satisfactory character. Large quantities of sash, doors, blinds and other building matertal are annually turned out ...

A HARD MAN TO BEAT

THE LIVE RAILROAD AGENT IS UP TO ALL SORTS OF TRICKS.

Circus People Are Pretty Cute Themselves, but This Story Shows How One Party Was Cleverly Outwitted by the Hustling Railroader.

"There are people who think you can't beat a circus man, but I want to tell you that the hardest man to do is a live railroad man."

The old sawdust manager had tried it. He continued:

"Know where Purcell is in the Indian Territory? Away down at the jumping off place on the Santa Fe road. The show had been at Purcell and we wanted to get out in the night for a long run. We were going to make a jump to Kansas City. Not far from Purcell is another town, Oklahoma City. At that point a competing road with the Santa Fe runs in. We had 500 people, and of course the railroad men were after us. It was a big haul. Some of our people bought through tickets from Purcell, and they didn't worry. But about 200, maybe more, of the crowd that always haggles over a 10 cent dicker concluded to take the Santa Fe from Purcell to Oklahoma City, pay the short haul, and then take the competing line at Oklahoma, the agents of which were active and full of promises.

"Then the Santa Fe man fixed it so the dickerers couldn't buy any tickets from Purcell to Oklahoma, for the train we were to go on was a special. The dickerers said that was all right; that they would wait for the regular. In less than five minutes a bulletin was slapped on the board of the station to the effect that the regular Santa Fe was 13 hours late. That made the fellows who were dickering for a cheaper rate turn white around their gills.

"In another five minutes I saw a man on a track velocipede scudding down the stretch. Every man to his business. So I thought the railroad people knew what they were doing, and they did. That chap on the velocipede was going down the track to flag the regular and hold it indefinite. Smart trick, wasn't it? Wait till I tell you. There was a smarter trick than that.

"When the special got ready to pull out, the dickerers asked the agent if they could pay on the train from Purcell to Oklahoma, and he said 'Cert.' So they all board the train at Purcell, intending to get off at Oklahoma. Just before the train pulled out the agent walks down to the engine and asks the old man at the throttle how long he had been on the road and about the capacity of his iron horse, and so forth.

"'How many miles an hour can she go at her best?' asked the agent.

"'On a good track, 65 miles.'

"'Is it a good track through Oklahoma City?'

"'Yes, pretty good.'

"'All right. You've got no orders to stop there nor to slow up, have you?'

"'Not yet.'

"'Well, when you get to the edge of the town you let her go. Don't stop for anything—flags or teams or cattle. Scoot through the town at a 65 mile gait or more ... until ... the ... desolation about 11 miles t'other side and you smoke a box of the finest cigars in Chicago. Is a go?'

"'If I don't get no orders 'fore I start.'

"'Well, you are five minutes late now.'

"In a minute and I calculate it was less, the circus special was under way. It went around curves like a scared snake. It shot across straight lines like a gazelle that had been singed. It whirled the rest of that country into the sky. After a while we saw a town. Then we went through it like the woman that's shot from the catapult, only more so. One of the dickerers, who was smiling to think the conductor had not yet come round, asked a brakeman as the train was going through the street, 'What town is this?' The brakeman said, 'Oklahoma City.'

"The dickerer's smile faded as it came, as the poet says, and his hair stood up, and turning to the brakeman he says:

"'Jezecrimini! Stop her! Here's where we get off.'

"'She doesn't even hesitate at a town like this,' said the brakeman.

"Well, about 11 miles on this side, in a strip of country where a crow can't live and where an Indian wouldn't be caught dead, that old iron horse began to slow up. The conductor came through just then and said:

"'Tickets!'

"Well, say, it was a funny sight. Them that had tickets showed up and then went to sleep. But the dickerers began to kick. They said they should have been let off at Oklahoma City. The conductor said the train didn't stop at Oklahoma, that it wasn't scheduled to stop there, and that he wasn't going to go back that trip. The leader of the dickerers for cheap fares wanted to know what was be done.

"The conductor was an old timer. He had a face on him like a woman who never loved anybody. He just told them, 'Pay or get off.' Then they asked him where they old pay to. And he said the train wouldn't stop any more until it got to Kansas City the next morning unless stopped to put them off. And he reached up and caught the bellcord.

"And every one of the dickerers paid to Kansas City. And, of course, under the railroad rules, they paid more than they would have paid if they had bought tickets at Purcell. And the company was that much ahead. And that's what I mean when I say that the hardest man to do is a live railroad man."—New York Sun.

According to the latest statistics the women in Sweden outnumber the men by 148,669.

NO USE FOR LADDERS.

THE RETIRED BURGLAR TELLS OF TWO UNFORTUNATE EXPERIENCES.

He Got Into and Out of the Houses With Ease, but That Wasn't All—How a Detective Got a Clew and Worked It—Escaped Once With a Broken Arm.

"Ladders, when you find them handy," said the retired burglar, "may seem like a very convenient way of getting into open second story windows, but after two experiences that I had with them I gave them up and stuck to the old fashioned way of doors and cellar windows.

"In a suburban town that I visited once I found 'em painting a Queen Anne house in the rainbow style that they used to paint houses in, and that, I suppose, they paint 'em in still to some extent. The men had ladders up, no stage, and I noticed that at the close of the day one of them was painting near a window, and I wondered if he'd leave his ladder there when he stopped work at night. I sauntered around that way after dark, and there it was, and it was summer, and the window was wide open. Most folks in the country, when their houses are being painted, are apt to be a little skittish about the ladders, and if one should be left like this one they'd be pretty sure to close the window near it and lock it, but these folks didn't appear to be disturbed, and as far as my getting into the house was concerned it was just about as easy for me to walk up that ladder and step off through the window as it would have been to walk in at the front door with it unlocked.

"Later, about 2 o'clock the next morning, I went up that ladder and in at the window without the slightest trouble, and there was nobody sleeping in that room. It was all just as easy as it could be. I poked around the house and gathered up what stuff there was worth carrying off and went back to that room and the open window and down the ladder and off.

"A month after that, as I was walking across the platform of a station on the same road that the other town was on to take a train, there was a man laid his hand on my arm and says, 'Now, don't make a fuss about it, and it'll be a good deal easier all around.' And I recognized in him the detective of the road, a man that I knew meant business, and I went along with him.

"Being a man of brains, he had gone up to the house where the robbery was as soon as he had heard of it, which was the day after. There he had put himself in the burglar's place and followed in his footsteps as near as he could. He had had the ladder placed in just the same position, and he had gone up that and stepped off into the window and followed over his track inside the house as close as he could guess at it, and then he'd come back to the window and got out on to the ladder, and so down to the ground.

"The ladder went up on the right hand side of this window, and while it was easy enough to reach it, still it was quite a little step from the sill to the ladder, and he noticed that when he had got his foot on the ladder he ... so that his elbow just touched it in the angle between the window frame and the clapboards. He gave a little push on that elbow naturally and threw himself out again on to the ladder. Then he stopped and looked at the spot where his elbow had touched. The paint was dry and there was no mark, but he called up the painters and learned that on the morning before—that was the morning after the house had been robbed—the paint at that place, on the cupboard by the window frame, and on the frame itself had been smudged a little, and they'd touched it over. That was all the detective wanted to know. From that time on he had been looking for a man with two paint spots of different colors on the left elbow of his coat, and I was the man.

"It may seem amazing to you that I hadn't rubbed the paint off. I had rubbed some of it off, and I was going to rub the rest off the next day, and then I kept setting that next day ahead, as we are apt to do, and I finally wound up by letting it go altogether, the rest of it. There wasn't one chance in a thousand of its leading to anything, and even as it was I might have talked myself out of the paint, but I had a watch that I'd got in the house in my pocket, and that settled it.

"That was one ladder. This was the other:

"Looking around the outside of a house in the country one night, I found a ladder lying on the ground against the rear of the house. They had some fruit trees in the garden, and I suppose they'd been working over them, or on the grape arbor maybe, and were going on with the work next day and had left the ladder out instead of taking it down cellar for the night. It was summer, and on the side of the house there were two windows open in one room. I thought I'd set the ladder up then and go in one of those windows. I set the ladder up and found it a little short, but by reaching up and getting a hold of the window sill and stepping up on the ends of the side pieces of the ladder I was able to get in tolerable easy. I went through the house and gathered up what there was to get and was turning to go from the last room when I knocked a picture over on a bureau and woke up the man that was sleeping in the room. I went back to the room I'd come in at and backed out the window and hung down for the ladder, and, by cracks, it wasn't there! But I'd got to go all the same, and I let go and dropped. I saw the ladder as I was going down at the next window. I'd got out the wrong window. I turned half over going down, struck on my left side and broke my arm.

"I got away that time, but I was laid up for six weeks, and after that I didn't fool any more with ladders."—New York Sun.

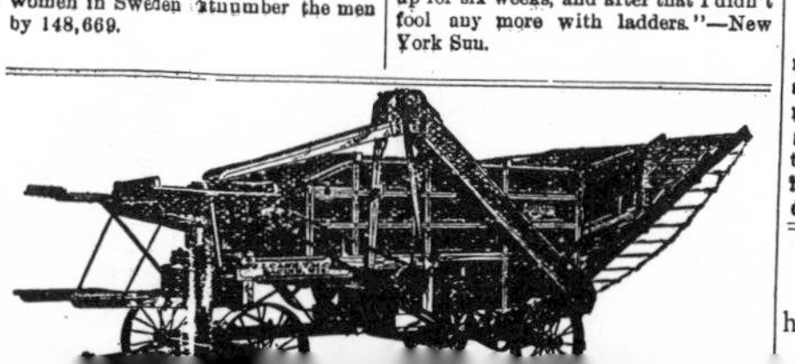

THE CONTINENTAL ...

An Appleton Business Concern in Marked Favor With Twin City People.

That a large majority of the men and boys of the Twin Cities purchase their clothing at Appleton is accounted for in the extremely liberal policy of the Continental Clothing House of that city, which is located at 805 College Avenue. This concern handles everything in outer and under garments that man or boy needs—in fact, clothes mankind from head to foot with everything excepting shoes, and they do it in such a pleasing and satisfactory manner that if one buys there once he is ce... ...nent patron T... N·enah and M... ...th the Continent... first place, Sa... is probably on... ...lers of clothin... ...nited States. He... ...lishments in his... , but as well at ... Avenue and Larrabee street), Springfield, Ill., Galesbury, Ill., and LaCross and Oshkosh, Wis. and his office at 1014 Medina Building, Chicago, is indeed a daily scene of great activity, for it is there Mr. Stern devotes his entire time to buying for his many stores. His purchases are necessarily very extensive, and as he controls almost the total output of several of the largest and best known manufacturers in the country, and has the cash in hand to take advantage of every possible discount, it is easily seen he makes his money go a long way in purchasing. For this reason his patrons can buy of him the very best, most stylish and durable goods at just about the same as is usually paid for shoddy at the average clothing house. The Continental is strictly a cash house, and as no poor accounts are accumulated, there is no loss to be distributed among those who pay as they go. Values are always at a maximum and prices at a minimum at the Continental. A dollar goes further at this house than a dollar and a half at some clothing concerns, and this is why Neenah and Menasha mankind pin their faith to the Continental. There is an immense stock of clothing, furnishing goods hats, etc., to select from, and no matter what your fancy of mind or condition of pocket-book, it can be fitted. Add to this most pleasing condition of things the fact that the Mitchell Bros., who are managers for Mr. Stern's Appleton house, together with all their employes, are most courteous and accommodating in all their dealings with the public, and the causes for success are at once apparent. The Continental carries a standing advertisement on the first page of THE DAILY NEWS, which will always be found of money-saving interest to our readers, as the concern is continually offering some exceptionally rare inducements to the people of the Twin Cities.

Street car fare is refunded all residents of the Twin Cities who make purchases to the extent of $2 or more.

WM. A. MASON.

An Expert Horseshoer With a Splendid Reputation.

Among the best-known and most accomplished horseshoers of this section is Wm. A Mason, commonly termed by those who know him intimately as "Billy." ... ...ience in th... ...de under C... and finishe... f Manitowoc ... years. He has been located here the past five years and has worked up a very large trade by his general excellence of work. Mr. Mason is not merely a horseshoer. He is also an expert in treating diseases of the hoof, having given this important branch of the business much scientific research, and as a consequence he enjoys a large trade. He is a native of Branch, Manitowoc county where he was born in 1872.

C. E. HILLIKER.

Twin City Representative of the "Milwaukee" Railroad.

Mr. Hilliker came to Neenah the first of last January and assumed charge of the passenger and freight business of the Chicago, Milwaukee & St. Paul Railroad company, and so pushing and progressive has he been that the business at this point is now in a much more satisfactory condition than formerly. Mr. Hilliker is an old railroad man in point of service, having been in the employ of the "Milwaukee" for many years. He is a native of Ontario, having been born in the village of Norwich, Oxford county, in 1863. He came to "the States" in 1882, and began his railroad career as a telegraph operator at Groton, South Dakota, where he had charge of a station about six years. He was then located at Aberdeen, in the same State, for 12 years, when he was transferred to Neenah.

G. F. ALWARD.

A Gentleman Who Has Made An Enviable Reputation for Himself.

Although Mr. Alward has been located in Appleton a few months, yet in that comparatively short time he has succeeded in firmly establishing himself in the good graces of the most substantial citizens, both in Appleton and the twin cities of Neenah and Menasha. Mr. Alward is the correspondent of Arthur R. Jones & Co., of Chicago, the well-known dealers in stocks, bonds, grain, provisions, etc., the house of Jones & Co., being among the largest and most responsible concerns of the west. Mr. Alward has splendid quarters in the Sherman House block, and as his place is connected with direct wires to New York, Boston and Chicago continnous market reports are posted instantaneously with all changes in the great commercial centers named, so that his patrons are catered to in a manner as satisfactory as if they were upon the floor of the great exchanges in Chicago or the east, and equally as advantageous and safe investments may be made right here at home. Mr. Alward is well posted in all that pertains to his business, and his judgment and advice is almost daily sought by many of our best-known people. Residents of Neenah and Menasha will find it to their material interest to consult Mr. Alward before making investments. He will be found a pleasant, agreeable and a safe man with whom to establish business relations. He is pleased at all times to extend every possible courtesy and favor to patrons. Telephone 133.

J. I. CASE THRESHING MACHINE CO.

... This Great Company's Branch House in Neenah.

About a year ago D. Schwieger, as general agent, came to Neenah and established a branch house for the great concern of J. I. Case Threshing Machine Co., of Racine, manufacturers of high class engines and threshing machines, and so successful has he been that the sales in the territory covered by the Neenah branch during the year amounted to nearly $100,000, certainly a satisfactory enough showing for the first year. But this comparatively remarkable business is easily accounted for, when it is known that the Case Company's engines and threshing machinery have for years stood at the head of the list, that they are positively the best that money, talent and experience can produce, and that Mr. Schwieger has had an experience in the threshing machine business of over 30 years. The annual output of this company foots up into the milions annually. As an instance of the company's business the statement is made that they manufac... and 1,000 horse powers. They are distributed throughout the United States and Canada by 31 general agents.

Their Neenah branch is to be a fixture, in order that their representative here may be permanently in touch with the large and prosperous agricultural class throughout northern Wisconsin. The company could not appoint a more capable, more experienced or better acquainted man than D. Schwieger, for he has lived in Wisconsin over 20 years and has many warm personal friends throughout the State. As before stated he has had an experience of over 30 years in this particular business, and up to the time of associating himself with the J. I. Case Co., two years ago had only been connected with two other concerns. This is a record any man might point to with pride. He is the right man in the right place, and as he is chock full of hard day's work is certain to materially increase his next year's business.

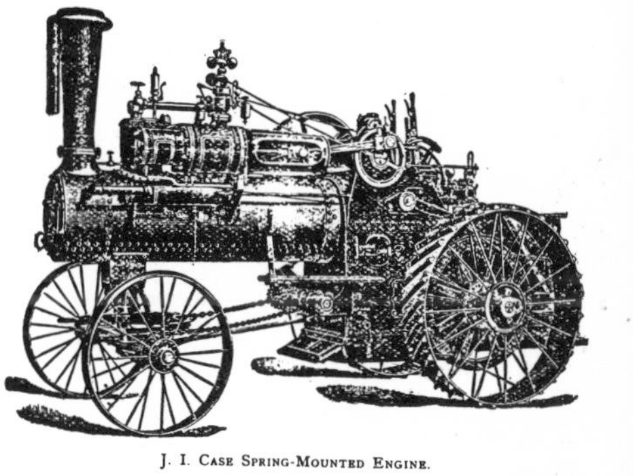

J. I. CASE SPRING-MOUNTED ENGINE.

J. M. THOMPSON.

An Old and Reliable Dealer in Flour, Feed, Coarse Grain Etc.

For more than forty-four years has J. M. Thompson been a resident of Neenah, 19 of which he has been in his present business, that of the sale of flour, feed, coarse grain, etc., in which he has been very successful.

Mr. Thompson was born in York State in 1837 and came to Wisconsin when seven years of age with his parents, settling on a farm a few miles from Milwaukee, in the town of Honey Creek. In 1854, at the age of 17, he moved to Neenah, where he has been a useful citizen since.

Looking the Matter Over.

"Have you considered the trouble we may have with people abroad if we annex these outlying islands?" "Not much," replied the matter-of-fact congressman. "But I have given some thought to the trouble we're likely to have with constituents at home if we don't."—Indianapolis Journal.

Phone your address and have The Daily News deliver-

Lord of the Knife

J.B. Murphy, Millionaire Surgeon
His Life in Pictures

by
Suzanne Hart O'Regan

Palmer Publications, Inc.

First edition.

Library of Congress Catalog Card Number
86-62952

ISBN: 0-910122-92-X

Printed in the United States of America
Palmer Publications, Inc.
Amherst, WI 54406

Suzanne Hart O'Regan
256 N. Park Avenue
Neenah, WI 54956

Contents

Dedication

For
Thomas,
Morgan,
Dustin and
Hadley

Acknowledgments

While I was seeking and identifying photographs to illuminate J.B.'s life and career the following people were most helpful: Dr. William S. Grimes, J.B.'s cousin; Marilyn Doty of the Neenah Library; Dee Dellem of the Menasha Library; Sue Zolkowski and CeCe Wiltzius of the Appleton Library; Nancy Campbell of the Theda Clark Regional Medical Center Library; Mara Munroe of the Oshkosh Library; Kristin Bjurstrom, Executive Director of Charitable, Educational and Scientific Foundations of the State Medical Society of Wisconsin; Archie Motley, Curator of Archives and Manuscripts of the Chicago Historical Society; Kimberly Chelos, Archivist of the Northwestern Memorial Group; Dorothy Darrow of the Chicago Golf Club; Rosemary Odmark of the Illinois Manufacturers Association; Dr. George Stevenson of the Murphy Memorial in Chicago; Roberta Dupuis and Julie O'Heir of Mercy Hospital, Chicago; Marquente Fallucco of the American Medical Association; John Bouch of the Chicago Medical Society; The Museum of Science and Industry; Sally Garmeski of the American College of Surgeons; Clark Nelson of the Mayo Clinic, Rochester, Minnesota; William Kona and Mary Jane Kirchner of Rush Presbyterian St. Luke's Medical Center; the staff of the Museum of Medical Progress in Prairie du Chien, Wisconsin; Dr. G.R. Anderson.

Friends from the Fox Valley generously gave me their time and photographs: Ded Bergstrom; Ray Wippick; Bill Dresser; Don Mitchell; George Larson; Cynthia Dery; Nancy Maas; Hazel Schmidt; Alfred Zellmer; Carl Kiekhaufer; and Mr. and Mrs. Leonard Larson.

A special word of thanks goes to Sister Mary Mark Kerin RSM (Aunt Margaret) for her editorial skill and to Mrs. George Hallas for her help.

I wish to express my gratitude particularily to Jeanette Hurley Reuben (Mrs. Don Reuben). Mrs. Reuben is J.B. Murphy's granddaughter and by sharing the family photographs she made this book possible.

I drew much information from Loyal Davis's book, *J.B. Murphy, Stormy Petrel of Surgery.*

Robert C. Ernest, President of Kimberly-Clark Corporation, arranged for the expert reproduction of the original Murphy photographs, thus making forever possible access to this valuable historical record through the Neenah Historical Society.

The masterly and elegant design which Bonnie Adams Neer gave to the cover will surely be a source of delight to the reader, as it was to the author.

My husband and daughters deserve my everlasting gratitude. Without their support and toleration I would not be able to spend so much time in the past.

Suzanne Hart O'Regan
View Pointe House
Neenah, Wisconsin
October, 1986

Lord of the Knife

J.B. Murphy, Millionaire Surgeon
His Life in Pictures
1857-1916

by Suzanne Hart O'Regan

I n the year of 1857, three years before the nation would be sundered by the Civil War, Ann Grimes Murphy welcomed into the frozen December of Wisconsin a new child, a boy.

Three brothers and two sisters had preceded John, but none came after him. John had the advantage of his mother's full attention. Ann Murphy was the first of several women whom fate sent to bless John Murphy's path.

John was born in a country of lovely spring and fall. Summer and winter, however, tried men's spirits; the summer demanded endless toil and the winter, endless endurance.

Ann and Michael Murphy rejoiced at their little son John; they could not foresee what cause the world would have to rejoice with them too. Ann Murphy was up and doing soon after her son's birth. She had to bake the bread, cure the meat, dry the beans, corn and peas, spin, weave, knit, mold the candles, and make the soap by bleaching lye from the winter's ashes and by adding lard. The only rest Ann Murphy had all day was when she sat down to milk cows.

The largest room in the Murphy house was the kitchen where the stove was, the only warm room. One other room downstairs was a small bedroom for Michael and Ann and the newest baby. The upstairs was all one room where the children slept. Everybody went to bed in the dark and got up in the dark. In the winter there was frost on the feather quilts.

John's family made a little money by baling corn husks and selling them in town. Practically everyone used corn husk mattresses in that era.

Children in 1857 were part of a farm family's work force. They fed calves, worked in the fields, raked, hoed, tied bundles of grain, picked up vegetables and fruit. They gathered raspberries, blackcaps, blackberries and wild strawberries, hazelnuts and hickory nuts.

In John's second spring, he watched his mother and older brothers spade a garden, plant and dig potatoes and carrots. Nearby was a wooden barn with a dirt floor; one horse and four cows were driven to and from the nearby pasture night and morning. The mother and children milked the cows and carried the full pails to the house.

Michael Murphy worked all his daylight hours converting wild land into tillable fields. All around him was dark forest, gloom and growths of tangled brush and thick stands of maple, beech, oak, elm and basswood. Many of the trees were five or six feet in diameter and some over a hundred feet tall. In a whole year he would do well to clear six or seven acres and still have left the task of breaking the land to the plow. Michael used a yoke of oxen to draw his heavy plow through the tough root-matted sod and the underground roots. After turning the sod, he left the turf to decompose for a year. By the third season a farmer could expect to plow with a single ox team.

With his older sons to help him, Michael also worked hard fencing their fields to keep out the cows and pigs that roamed free. They made a rail fence by quartering logs and laying the pieces one on top of another along a zig-zag line. They planted corn for the family and the animals, supplementing this food with wheat, vegetables, pigs, hens and sheep. The cows provided milk and butter.

The family scattered the wheat seed by hand. Then in the fall they cut the standing grain with scythe and cradle, raked it and bound it into sheaves. A man could cradle no more than three acres a day. Oxen were led back and forth over the sheaves to separate the grain or seeds from the straw.

J.B. was raised in a world of steady industry where the lack of convenient aids and tools demanded great resourcefulness.

These immigrant Irish, Michael and Ann, wanted a better life for their children than they had seen for themselves. Accordingly when the one-room school house had done all it could do for the little Murphys, their parents were willing to do without their children's help. In his turn John went to the town of Appleton to live with his mother's cousin, Mrs. Driscoll, at the southwest corner of Catherine Street and College Avenue. John went to the Hercules High School and found a job working in Alexander Lewis' Drug Store on the corner of South College Avenue and East Oneida Street. Working in a drug store then included more than selling ready-made prescriptions. While some drugs were imported in crude form from the East, most of the tinctures and extracts had to be made up from roots and herbs that the druggist and his assistant would personally gather in the vicinity. Dr. J.R. Reilly had an office over the drug store at 199 College Avenue, and he influenced John to select a medical career.

All the children of Ann and Michael Murphy were born under a particular star of accomplishment. At a time and in a situation where most people considered grade school more than sufficient, these children were motivated to seek more. Daniel became a priest, Lucinda a nun, and Frank a pharmacist, Michael a big land owner in the Dakotas, and Ellen married a railroad conductor, the equivalent of today's jet pilot.

J.B. went to Rush Medical School in Chicago in 1878. At this time being a medical student was easy. Entrance requirements were lower than they were for a good high school. It was possible to graduate without having ever touched a patient, having heard only "lectures." The most stringent requirement was the ability to read and write but many schools accepted less if the student could pay the fees. Certainly for J.B., the greatest challenge was getting the tuition together. His mother gave him the money she had saved by selling the fur pelts her sons had shot. The cost was $64 a year.

John loved Chicago! He loved the power and the energy alive in this heart of the Midwest that had the wharves of New York and Boston. Chicago was a major port of the world with the Great Lakes to the North and East and the mighty Mississippi River system waiting to carry the produce South and West. In Chicago men were judged by what they could do rather than who their fathers were. Here the Irish found advancement easier than ever before.

John Murphy proved to be a student clearly above his fellows and he caught the eye of his professor, Dr. Edward W. Lee. Dr. Lee had a drug store at 260 South Halsted Street and upon graduation Dr.

. . . graduated from the Appleton High School in 1876, and received the degree Doctor of Medicine from Rush Medical College in 1879.

Murphy began his practice in the wooden structure that housed this drug store. J.B. roomed at the home of Dr. Lee's brother at Harrison Street and Racine Avenue. Drs. Lee and Murphy had an early insurance program where some patients paid $1.00 a month, no matter how often or seldom they came to the office.

In late July, 1881, **Ann Murphy** wrote John of the illness of his father and then immediately following came a message that his father was dead. He died on the Winnebago County farm that he had pioneered. Of course, J.B. hurried home. After the funeral, Ann Murphy pushed a leather money sack into her boy's hand. She knew his dream was more education and she gave him the chance. It was her joy to see her child advance in the world.

In 1882, American medicine was far behind that of Europe. His mother's gift made it possible for J.B. to study in Vienna, Berlin and the University of Heidelberg. German medical science was the unchallenged "superior" in the medical world when J.B. studied there.

Between 1870 and 1914, 15,000 American doctors undertook some form of serious study abroad. J.B. had to be very frugal as the minimum cost of study for a year in Germany was between $700 and $800.

J.B. returned to Chicago in the spring of 1884. He was 26, handsome, well-dressed with polished manners. Besides, he was better educated than 90 per cent of the American medical community.

Many people came to the little West Side office of Lee and Murphy. By temperament J.B. worked to excess; he had the emotional wherewithall, the energy and stamina, the ambition and the intellectual power to be a great man. Practice had trained his senses to recognize and his mind to interpret with astonishing accuracy the clues nature left on a sick man. In those years, poorly cooked food, unheated drafty houses, over-exertion, exposure to cold and snow and floods, lack of adequate sanitation, ignorance and superstition nourished a bountiful crop of ills in Chicago. J.B. wanted to do surgery, but he could not support himself by surgery alone because there was not enough of it. So he handled his share of the City's child births, indigestion, kidney trouble, and typhoid fever, measles, whooping cough and the dread diphtheria. Yet it was surgery J.B. wanted.

The general attitude toward surgery contributed to high mortality, as the knife was considered a last resort; the patient waited until he was in a dying condition before he would submit to an operation. The layman tried to act as his own doctor. He carried buckeye or pieces of potato; he wore bags of asafoetida or camomile to ward off illness. Some even bled themselves every spring to get rid of their "bad blood." Others sent for quack nostrums advertised in the newspapers.

The malady we call appendicitis was then called "perityphlitis" or "cholera morbus." Yet what caused it and how to treat it was unknown. The patient with this ailment usually died in a few days.

When J.B. started to operate, it was mostly a matter of repair work on the surfaces and extremities of the body; sometimes accidents provided the chief need for surgery. This field of medicine was indeed far from the well-ordered world it would become. J.B. began in the era of so-called "kitchen surgery," performed in the patient's home on the kitchen table, or the parlor sofa or a door taken from its hinges and laid across two saw-horses. Even by 1880 the ideas of Lord Lister about germs were generally believed to be an outlandish new fad. Microbes were believed to be fantasy, and antiseptic cleanliness was beyond the comprehension of most people. Instruments were carried in a little case or loose in a vest pocket; they were held over the steam from a kettle when sterilization was called for.

The people of Chicago liked J.B. Murphy. They felt that here was a doctor who knew what he was talking about, with no "hemming and hawing." He knew right off what was wrong and what ought to be done about it and he told the patient straight out. J.B.'s practice grew. He was a prime favorite with the numerous Irish Catholics. When they became sick, they sent for the priest, a jug of whiskey and Dr. Murphy.

The prominent Ambrose Plamondon family were Dr. Lee's patients. However, when young George Plamondon arrived at the office to ask Dr. Lee to come and see his sister Jeanette, the powerful hand of fate stepped in, and the second woman who would help J.B. was introduced into his life. Dr. Lee could not get away; his assistant went in his place.

Dr. Murphy found Ambrose Plamondon's beautiful daughter dying of typhoid. At a time when death walked triumphant and rarely found his entrance barred, J.B. did battle with death for Jeanette. His education, vigor, and will made her rally. Together they held death away and achieved their first victory together. Jeanette's parents witnessed this young physician go into the valley of the shadow and bring back to them their apparently lost child. With Jeanette's life, J.B. won her parents and somewhere in the struggle Jeanette and John won each other.

Doctor J.B. married his patient on November 25, 1885, in St. Patrick's Church in Chicago. She was rich and well-connected with "Society." He would become so. He needed someone like Jeanette to take care of his life and home. She would do so. He needed a companion to bear some of the burden of a rising surgeon . . . someone with power yet one who would seem like a well-protected flower. Jeanette proved to be that darling companion.

Ambrose Plamondon and his wife blessed the marriage by purchasing the house next to their own for the young couple.

J.B. became a public figure when a bomb was thrown during a labor rally. It began on May 4, 1886 when a group of factory workers and their families had gathered in Haymarket Square in Chicago some time in the afternoon. Around 10:45 p.m. policemen came in and told the crowd to go home. Then someone threw a bomb. J.B. was called to the police station where 70 policemen lay wounded. He operated on these victims for hours. That night's blood made J.B.'s knife famous in Chicago.

Thirteen months after her wedding Jeanette gave birth to an apparently healthy son. In 1887 death stood nearby when new life began. Therefore, the relatives felt blessed and spared when all went well with the arrival of the baby. Death had been put off twice. John Murphy had battled typhoid and won Jeanette; Jeanette braved birth and won a son. Death, however, gathered his forces again. When John's son was six weeks old, he was smiling, looking into his father's eyes and growing bigger every day. He was his Mother's pride, his Father's joy—their love made visible. John and Jeanette's hearts were bound to this child, his face and sound were cut into their eternity. Then death came. This time neither wealth nor will nor learning could defeat the invader. Death came into this house of deep carpets and security and love. Death broke the circle and carried the boy's life away.

John and Jeanette buried their heir in his Grandfather Plamondon's tomb in Calvary Cemetery. The grave haunted them even unto their own graves.

Had her son lived, Jeanette might have become just another conventionally dependent matron but with his death she pointed her life in the direction of her husband's quest—his career.

Eighteen eighty-seven also brought death to J.B.'s sister Lucinda (Sister Mary Constantia), to his brother Daniel, a priest, and to his brother Frank, a pharmacist. All three died of pulmonary tuberculo-

Then death came. This time neither wealth nor will nor learning could defeat the invader. Death came into this house of deep carpets and security and love . . .

sis. Ann Murphy buried her children next to their father in St. Patrick's Cemetery in Neenah. Ann found her comfort in her faith and her God.

Off in Chicago, John worked like never before. It seemed as if work became his revenge on death. The weapons J.B. forged in medicine kept death from having his will completely; he kept thousands safe from the loss that he himself endured. He put a laboratory in the barn back of his house and spent much time there operating and experimenting. Finally he rented an office at No. 93 Adam Street in the heart of the city. Even though he and Dr. Lee were no longer partners, they remained fast friends.

In 1889 baby Jeanette was born.

J.B.'s study and experiments and finally surgery on his patients led him to establish this principal, "For all practical purposes typhlitis, perityphlitis, perityphlitic tumor and perityphlitic abscess mean *inflammation of the vermiform appendix:* the chief danger of this infection is *perforation,* perforation in the great majority of cases produces a circumscribed, supperative peritonitis, tending to become generalized; in the light of our present knowledge. The surgical treatment of this lesion offers the best chance for the life and future health of the patient and the process of the disease needs to be watched with knife in hand."

In 1890 baby Cecile was born and on November 18, 1892 Mildred arrived.

J.B. was determined to prove to the medical world that early operative treatment was the only way to save the lives of those suffering with appendicitis. He set out to make the world "appendicitis conscious." How completely he accomplished this the whole world knows!

In 1892 Dr. Murphy accepted a professorship of surgery at the College of Physicians and Surgeons; he moved into the Venetian Building and by June he had devised a button that allowed the two ends of a cut intestine to be joined together in half a minute creating a complete anastomosis. Truax, Green and Company manufactured the "Murphy Button" which was soon in demand by surgeons all over the country.

In 1893 the five-year-old girl Jeanette Murphy died. J.B. could call to her, and the child had no living ears to hear. The mother took this death hard and it became J.B.'s duty to comfort and restore, if he could, a broken woman.

After this child's death J.B. and Jeanette moved their family to Michigan Avenue just south of Thirty-first Street and J.B. began practicing at Mercy Hospital.

John and Jeanette's youngest child Celeste arrived on January 13, 1897.

J.B. and Jeanette would make one more house move and that was in 1900 when they moved two blocks down Michigan Avenue to No. 3305.

After twelve years of marriage John and Jeanette had stood together at the cradles of five babies, at the graves of two. For these little ones, that God spared, the parents were thankful.

Sister Mary Raphael McGill had been the administrator at Mercy Hospital for 13 years when she met Dr. John B. Murphy in 1895. Sister Raphael had heard of J.B. as the young surgeon who had attended the wounded of the Haymarket Square incident and testified at the subsequent trial. Also one of the Mercy Sisters in Chicago had consulted Dr. Murphy regarding swollen glands in her neck. Dr. Murphy recommended surgery as they were tubercular, but since he was not on Northwestern University's staff, he was unable to operate at Mercy Hospital. However Sister Raphael listened to Dr. Murphy's arguments and arranged for a change in the "staff privileges policy."

" . . . and the process of the disease needs to be watched with knife in hand."

"One must think about each case and reason it out, pathology, causation and treatment; but one must not try to group them. The individual bearings must be taken every time."

In *Service to Chicago* a Sister-nurse recalled, "The first time I saw Dr. John B. Murphy . . . he was riding on an elevator at Mercy Hospital with the superior, Sister Mary Raphael McGill. He wore an overcoat with a cape, one of the points thrown up over his left shoulder. He held a silk hat in his hand . . . Murphy was out looking up a suitable situation . . . Northwestern University had a contract with Mercy Hospital for the use of the wards and operating rooms and no doctor could use these, only Northwestern men.

"Dr. Murphy told Sister Raphael that if she would fix up an operating room according to his ideas, he would come to Mercy Hospital and use the private rooms for his patients. When I met them, they were looking for a site for an operating room. They decided on an alcove on the fourth floor. Work was commenced at once." Sister Raphael and Dr. Murphy remained fellow-workers for 20 years, until they both died in 1916. Sister Raphael was remembered thus, "As a superior, Sister Raphael was uniformly kind and generous. As a financier, she had no equal . . . She invariably got the best of every bargain. Her long experience made her wise, deliberate and shrewd."

With his operating room completed and staffed, Dr. Murphy started bringing his patients to Mercy. The hospital census began to swell and the publicity that surrounded J.B. Murphy swirled around Mercy Hospital. J.B. had the coolness, forecast and capacity to introduce revolution. He was a rebuke as well as a stumbling block to lesser people.

As for Sister Raphael, all J.B. asked of a hospital she would readily grant, because she thought he was right. She cast her vote with his view and it paid off for Mercy and for mankind. J.B.'s surgery was helped immeasurably by the discovery of anesthesia. Anesthesia swept the barrier of pain from the path of surgery, and this innovation cleared the road to surgical horizons unseen. In the beginning, however, the dangers of ether and chloroform were not appreciated. Death and the surgeon's knife were so often linked that all deaths were assumed to be from the ordeal of surgery. At that time anesthesia was achieved only with ether or chloroform. Chloroform was given by saturating a sponge and holding it over the patient's nose and mouth until he became unconscious. Ether was poured drop-by-drop on a few thicknesses of gauze laid over a piece of wire matting stretched on a frame above the patient's nose. When the patient stopped struggling, the doctor would tell whoever was dripping the ether to stop for a while. If the patient started moving again, the assistant would let a few more drop fall on the mask.

J.B. was ahead of his fellow surgeons in his appreciation of the dangers of anesthesia and realizing the importance of a good anesthetist. When Dr. Murphy came to Mercy Hospital he insisted on having a Sister in charge of anesthesia. Sister Mary Ethelreda O'Dwyer, a member of the first class to graduate from Mercy's nursing school, became his anesthetist. Sister Ethelreda's steady anesthetic technique reduced the death rate of surgery at Mercy.

Sister Mary Victorine Lippert was Doctor Murphy's surgical nurse for over ten years. Her notebooks preserved at Mercy list the steps to be followed in preparing for Dr. Murphy's cases. They are marvels of attention to detail. In his papers entitled, *Clinics* J.B. often referred to Sister Victorine's dedication and to his confidence in her.

J.B. was more successful in his occupation than other men were in theirs; hence he was more fortunate in this world's goods. People who had struggled felt a kinship with him. Also J.B. was in the right place at the right time. Chicago was a name synonymous with opportunity and J.B. was busy creating American medicine in his own image.

J.B. even ventured into neurological surgery when others feared to try. He pioneered in the suturing of arteries and veins, surgery of bones, joints and tendons. He advocated the use of nitrogen gas in the production of artificial pneumothorax. In 1912 he published the first issue of *Murphy's Surgical Clinics* which described his various operations and reproduced his lectures at Mercy Hospital.

The *Surgical Clinics* came into being due to the demand for publication of J.B.'s clinical presentations. The Saunders Company published *Surgical Clinics of John B. Murphy, M.D. at Mercy Hospital, Chicago*. These were a great help to the surgeons of J.B.'s day and they are a wonderful record today of J.B.'s conversation, his pride and his preferences.

In 1914 J.B.'s relatives in Wisconsin sent him word that strong-hearted, black-eyed Ann Murphy was dying. J.B. rode the passenger train to Neenah, Wisconsin, walked in mud and ice to a buggy and drove eight miles out to the old log farm house where he was born.

John took his mother's two hands. They talked, homey and heart-warming talk. He held the hands that had been good to him, so long ago. Mother and son put their arms around each other. Ann told her son, "I'm mighty proud of ye, Johnny, that I am." For the last time they looked each other in the eyes, and there they found no fault.

J.B. buried his mother beside his father, brothers and sister in the old Catholic cemetery on the edge of Neenah. Nowadays a huge stone bearing only the word "Murphy" marks the place. It stands brooding upon the many graves surrounding it. He had tried to praise this honorable woman with love and worship by erecting a great rock of granite. Had J.B. lived longer he would have had it inscribed, "Ann Grimes Murphy." His death so soon following his mother's left her name uncut on the stone J.B. had bought for her.

On August 1, 1914 Dr. and Mrs. J.B. Murphy and Dr. and Mrs. Charlie Mayo sailed from Liverpool for New York on board the *S.S. Mauretania*. On this trip the crew camouflaged the ship by draping tarpaulins of canvas over the sides, covered the port holes with blankets and ran in darkness at night. The night before landing, the ship changed course abruptly and came in at Halifax instead of New York. The British cruiser *Essex* had alerted the *Mauretania* to a German raider and to avoid it they changed course.

Fate loved to put J.B. in the spotlight and soon he was there with President Roosevelt.

Theodore Roosevelt ran for his third term as President in 1912. While on the campaign trail in Milwaukee, Roosevelt left the Gilpatrick Hotel on the evening of October 12th: Suddenly he was shot in the chest by an insane man. Roosevelt was saved by his steel spectacle case and his folded speech which absorbed the bullet's full impact. Nevertheless, the bullet did pierce his chest. Roosevelt insisted on driving to the auditorium and speaking. When he had finished, he was taken in an ambulance to the Emergency Hospital. From there he took a train to Chicago to see J.B. Murphy. Much trouble resulted from the fact that people in the audience had taken it upon themselves to call several doctors in Chicago to meet the Roosevelt train. However the ex-President wanted only one doctor to be in charge and following the advice of Dr. Joseph Colt Bloodgood of the John's Hopkins Hospital in Baltimore, he chose J.B. J.B. was the only one provided with the correct time and place of arrival, so he met the train and took the patient right to Mercy Hospital. Other disappointed medical men claimed that Murphy "stole" Roosevelt from them. The X-rays are still at Mercy to be seen. While the world called for surgery to remove the bullet, J.B. chose a policy of watchful waiting rather than risk blood poisoning. Roosevelt and the bullet grew old together. J.B.'s decision proved a wise one.

Roosevelt and Murphy became friends and remained so until death.

In 1912 J.B. and Jeanette bought a two-story building that had been built on the Mercy grounds to house an outpatient clinic. They

For the last time they looked each other in the eyes, and there they found no fault.

14

At the laying of the cornerstone October 23, 1923, William J. Mayo spoke: "This is a fiting monument to the greatest surgeon of his day, John B. Murphy, one of the founders of the College who gave unsparingly of his strength and talents to aid in the establishment of the organization, and whose noble spirit will always sanctify this ground."

remodeled and lavishly outfitted this building so J.B. could conserve his strength and his time because J.B. was suffering such severe attacks of angina pectoris that he was not able to continue his former pace.

It was heartbreak time at 3305 Michigan Avenue and at Mercy Hospital. The final dooms were weaving. The family and friends felt apprehensions of harm to J.B. from a hidden enemy, an enemy that despite all the advances of medicine, stood beyond the reach of any medicine of 1916. J.B. had carried the heavy load and saved many from agony; now his life's grip was slimmer than a cobweb thread.

He and Jeanette left the city and went to the scene of many happy times, the Chicago Golf Club out in Wheaton. There Jeanette hoped he would find rest as he had in former days. But it was not to be. The heat of July was defeating him as his body failed him.

In an attempt to escape the heat, Jeanette and J.B. took a Pullman car to Mackinac Island. That night it rained and cooled off. J.B. said he felt he had been resurrected. But he knew that the final struggle was upon him. Death would win.

J.B. told his friend Dr. Keefe, "I want a postmortem made after my death. You will find plaques of calcification in my aorta and destruction of its lining membrane. Those changes have been produced by an infection of long standing somewhere in my body. There are two other points I want checked carefully: my appendix, because I had appendicitis when I was a boy, and when I was in Germany studying I had a kidney infection; so look carefully at my kidneys."

On Friday, August 11th in the afternoon, J.B. said to his two visiting friends Drs. MacArthur and Keefe, "Help me into Jeanette's room, will you?" Realizing his weakness, they said, "We'll ask her to come in here. You mustn't exert yourself." But J.B. would have his way. He struggled, got to his feet, his friends hurried to help him walk. As they approached Jeanette's door, she came out. Pain and the rising mist made it almost impossible for him to see Jeanette. Yet he would see her again. Driven to the very end, J.B. knew what he wanted. As he walked he fought off unimagineable pain.

Jeanette, still a beautiful woman, ran toward J.B. What he had set out to do, J.B. had done. He was with Jeanette, but the rising mist obscured his vision. Death had come. To a far country, to a land whence no man returns, death took the child of Ann Grimes and Michael Murphy, the Wisconsin boy who found distant suns and mighty stars to live by, whose name even before he died had become a legend woven with men's struggle against illness the world over. J.B. had done his work and made his place. He did not fear to die, especially with Jeanette beside him.

The day was Saturday, August 12, 1916. By wagon or buggy, luxurious auto, Tin Lizzy, and railroad car something like several thousand people had come into Chicago from all parts of the Northwest.

Slowly, at 3305 Michigan Avenue, a procession moved in and out of the mansion. They had come to see one last time the face of J.B. Murphy. Now passed those who had known him long; those who worked with him and those to whom his skill had proved a saving grace.

On August 14, 1916 the procession moved with its hearse to St. James Roman Catholic Church and from there to Calvary Cemetery. There on the green lawn within the sound of the great lapping waters of Lake Michigan the crowded mourners heard Bishop Muldon preach the funeral sermon.

The body of J.B. Murphy rested forever. But the truth he struggled for and found would go on to bless the ages. The children of the vast and irreckonable future would have fewer bodily terrors to endure because John B. Murphy had lived.

J.B. Murphy's Youth
1857-1878

I n a cabin such as this, built by his father's hands, J.B. Murphy arrived; in December, in Wisconsin.

These two photos show St. Mary's Church on the corner of State and Seventh Street in Appleton. If it was a clearer photo we might recognize the youthful J.B. going in to attend mass with his family.

For reasons lost in time the Murphys went to church in Appleton but were buried in St. Patrick's cemetery in Neenah.

When J.B. was thirteen a Neenah photographer, C.B. Manville, dragged his cumbersome photographic equipment to a rooftop to record the Neenah of J.B.'s youth. The mills in this photo are still producing flour but very soon they would be adapted to accommodate the new product of the Fox River valley's water power—paper.

A remarkable aspect of this scene in Neenah in 1880 is the absence of anything disposable. The Menasha Woodenware barrels and bushel baskets will do service again and again. Likewise the employee's aprons will be washed and used until they become rags and from there perhaps to rugs. "Waste not, want not" and "use it up, use it out, use it over" would have been familiar admonitions to those who posed in this picture.

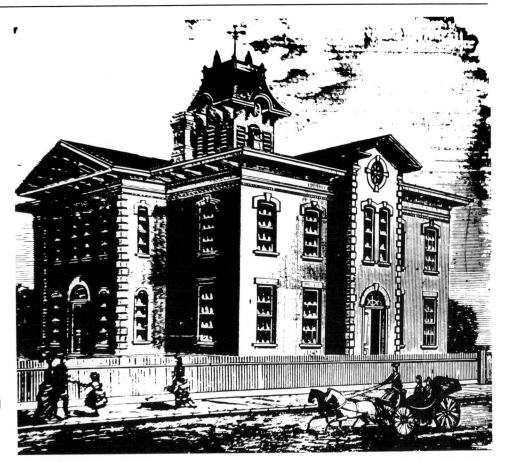

In 1872 J.B. graduated from the county school. In the Fall he went to board in Appleton with his mother's widowed cousin, Mrs. Driscoll, at the southwest corner of Catherine Street and College Avenue. J.B. attended Hercules High School when it looked much like this drawing.

This photo of downtown Appleton was taken 15 years after J.B. worked here for the town druggist, Alexander Lewis, and for the physician and surgeon, Dr. J.R. Reilly.

The picture was taken to immortalize the motion of the world's first electric streetcar as it ran in front of Pettibone's Dry Goods store.

Note the cast iron hitching posts.

In 1885, when the Civil War was twenty years past, the Grand Army of the Republic veterans would meet for songs and speeches: Then everyone would troop out to the village cemetery to lay lilacs on the graves of the departed veterans. The old gentlemen would tell war stories until it seemed to the children that the whole affair had taken place in the next county just a few years ago.

In the photo taken in Neenah, Civil War veterans, their mothers, wives and daughters have gathered to remember and celebrate "The Great Conflict."

This is a "surrey with the fringe on top." It was a specifically American vehicle and had curtains, a storm apron and lamps. It was a four (or more) seater family carriage. In this case the family had rented this rig from the livery stable and the livery owner's child stands to the right. A board sidewalk is visible in the center.

This picture had much information written on the back but the scribe failed to identify the imposing background building. Clearly he could not imagine that anyone would fail to recognize it.

This picture is a pretty rural style review of three generations.

No doubt these ladies sewed up their own fashions. Perhaps they had sent to Sears and Roebuck and ordered from this advertisement: "The grandest bargain we have to offer is this, our Minnesota, complete with the automatic drop desk cabinet with all modern attachments, everything that goes with a sewing machine and all for $27.45, crated, packed and delivered on board the cars in Chicago, free of charge."

The fancy belt buckles on the three older women could also be ordered, "Ladies' fine plated belt buckles, either in gilt or silver, complete with slide. Each 11¢."

This is a new gable front and wing folk Victorian farmhouse that was so loved and admired by its owners that they got dressed up and posed in front of it one Spring day.

Even with all the washing, sewing, gardening, cleaning, soapmaking and the terrible drudgery of huge meals three times a day, this good woman has found the time and energy to plant some flowers in a yard container.

The oldest boy is wearing short pants with his suit coat; so he is probably under 12 years of age. However, his is a more grown-up style than that of the next brother who is wearing a "military reefer" suit with a large collar made very stylish and bound all around with wide military braid.

Their sister has on black stockings and a madras cloth dress. The dress is likely homemade as her dress-bow and hair-bow match. The little brother has stockings, short pants and a blouse appropriate for little boys. Mama is holding the baby who regardless of sex would wear a long dress until able to walk.

The mother is dressed in somber color and she appears to have sacrificed her teeth on the altar of childbearing.

The chair on the porch is a spindle, bowback, hardwood kitchen or dining room chair. It cost about 38¢ in 1897.

College of Physicians and Surgeons, West Harrison and Honore Streets

Rush Medical College, 761 West Harrison Street

Mercy Hospital—Showing Old Building, Corner Twenty-Sixth Street and Calumet Avenue.

This building was originally built by the Sisters of Mercy as St. Agatha's Academy, a boarding school.

In the summer of 1863 they moved the pupils to a new building on Wabash Avenue, and this large brick structure with two and one-half acres of land became Mercy Hospital.

When J.B. lived in Chicago there were many massive and grand buildings that time has destroyed. Fortunately with the truthfulness of the camera and the art of the printer we can again see the towering structures, substantial and beautiful skyscrapers, elegant private residences, crowded thoroughfares and magnificent parks and monuments.

The Auditorium Building was at once a grand opera house, a superb hotel and a mammoth office building. An early guidebook describes the Auditorium: "It is in construction representative of Chicago as a city, where art, beauty and utility are so strongly defined though nearly always blended on every side. Cost of the building with ground, $5,500,000."

Auditorium Building and Annex, Michigan Avenue and Congress Street

Designed by Richard Morris Hunt, 1905 Prairie Avenue for Marshall Field in 1873.
Marshall Field was shrewd, honest, and incorruptible. He was the sharpest merchant in the United States, but the customer was always right. Marshall Field walked to work, followed by his carriage in dubious weather, because he thought driving would be ostentatious.

Marshall Field and George Pullman lived just a block apart and Marshall Field was a member of the Pullman Palace Car Company.
George Pullman's house was accepted in 1882 as the grandest house on Prairie Avenue.

Potter Palmer drained a marsh, arranged for the city to run a roadway through this lake frontage area and created Lake Shore Drive. He built his house facing the lake, looking toward Lincoln Park to the north and the City Harbor to the south. From 1882 to 1885 the work went on and the cost passed one million dollars. It was built of Wisconsin granite with Ohio sandstone and had a tower with a spiral staircase.

In 1892 J.B.'s daughter, Mildred was born and Francis Willard hired John Wellborn Root to design this monument to the Women's Christian Temperance Union at the southeast corner of La Salle and Monroe Streets.

Life of Opulence

Thursday, November 26, 1885
Chicago Tribune

When Jeanette and J.B. met, Jeanette lay near death from typhoid fever and Dr. Lee, the Plamondon family physician, allowed his new partner, Dr. Murphy, to take the case.

J.B. saved Jeanette's life and thus won her parents' hearts and later that of their beautiful daughter.

Ambrose Plamondon and his wife conferred about John Murphy. They concluded that he was an educated, intelligent gentleman, serious, energetic, sober, forthrightly honest and professionally able. This was the man for their Jeanette.

When Jeanette was only eighteen, she married the man of her choice. As far as we know, she never regretted giving her life to J.B. Murphy.

When they were married, J.B. had already begun his career as a medical teacher when he was appointed Lecturer in Surgery in Rush Medical College in 1884.

Mrs. J.B. Murphy, a leader of the Grand March at the Charity Ball of the Catholic Woman's National League.

Jeanette is wearing a cream lace evening dress with sequins. The bodice of such a dress appears to drape naturally. In reality it is very carefully tailored; each seam and hidden dart is boned. The lace outer dress is sewn onto a heavy cotton base.

The ostrich feather and immense corsage complete the evening dress attire of this young society matron.

In 1907 Mrs. Potter Palmer led the Grand March.

The wall of the staircase which Jeanette and John ascended with their candle was long ago demolished; the house where their babies died has likewise perished. Many things which people imagined would last forever are gone.

This house which Mr. and Mrs. Plamondon had given their daughter and new son-in-law, at 36 Throop Street, was a Richardson Romanesque type. Rough-faced stone work faced the street with brick used for the other three sides. A wide rounded Romanesque arch protected the entryway. Three plain sash windows dominate the second floor. The mansard roof provided a background for the wall dormer. On either side of the dormer window was a latticework design; a tree of life pattern and a roof top balustrade top it all off in exuberant style.

Wednesday, May 5, 1886

DEAD AND DYING

Viewing the field of the Terrible Slaughter in Chicago.

Results of the Anarchist Outbreak.

Police and Rioters Who Fell Together.

Today Devoted to Tearing Down the Red Flags.

Officers Raiding the Meeting Places of the Offenders of the Law.

Unable to Estimate the Number of Dead Anarchists.

Bold Attempt to Punish a Business Man Who Was Charged With Being an Informer.

CHICAGO, May 5—[Special]—Mob violence again asserted itself in the south-western part of the city this morning. About 9 o'clock groups of men, women and children began to gather at the corner of Eighteenth Street and Center Avenue and these groups soon aggregated three thousand persons. On one of the corners is the drug store of Samuel Rosenfeld. It became apparent that the owner of the store was the object against whom the crowd was bent on venting its spite. The men surged toward the building with threats and violent language. "Tear down the place!" they yelled. "Kill Rosenfeld; he's a police

The tragedy recalled to mind by the name "Haymarket Square" in reality occurred to the north of the monument on Desplaines Street. The statue of a policeman was put up to recall the events of the night of May 4, 1886. During a meeting of working men an unknown person threw a bomb into six companies of approaching policemen.

The night of the bombing Dr. John Murphy operated on most of the seventy wounded policemen. This surgery and his subsequent testimony in the anarchist trial was the beginning of his fame in Chicago.

In 1890 clothing modeled on sailor's suits was popular for both boys' and girls' wear. Jeanette stands on a carpet in her yard wearing a blue sailor dress with white trim. The absurdly large bow was considered perfect for young girls.

This photo was taken around the time that baby Cecille arrived. The wicker doll carriage and toy doll were given to Jeanette in an attempt to convince her that an infant's arrival was an asset to the household. Despite the elaborate preparations, Jeanette does not appear to be enthusiastic about the addition.

Baby Cecille has a ring on one tiny finger as she clings to the table provided by the Stevens photographer in McVickers Building. Also located in the McVickers Building was a luxurious soda parlor, "Gunthers." No doubt many young folks were lured into "one more smile" with the promise of a trip to "Gunthers."

Cecille is dressed in a "wrapper cloak" of cream-colored wool. Her fitted cap is made of cream flannel and lace.

Eight little riding pupils mounted on donkeys (the girls sidesaddle) with their instructor and his patient horse gaze at us from the long vanished year of 1891.

Second from left is J.B.'s daughter, Jeanette; on the far right are Florence and Al Amberg, Jeanette's first cousins.

Written on the back of the photo, "Father had 'Jimmie,' the donkey, sent to Leland from Colo. Springs."

Medical opinion of 1890 advised those suffering from T.B. symptoms to live in a dry climate, therefore J.B. went to Colorado Springs in 1890 leaving his practice in the care of Dr. Wit and Dr. Hartmann, his assistants. When the Colorado Springs climate did not prove dry enough, he went to Las Vegas. There his wife and two daughters joined him. After eight months of recuperation, J.B. returned to Chicago to become Professor of Surgery at The College of Physicians and Surgeons.

STEVENS McVICKERS THEATRE BLDG
CHICAGO
EXTRA FINISH

This picture was taken around 1891, shortly after J.B. came back to Chicago from Las Vegas. His wife and two daughters had spent eight months with him while J.B.'s health improved in the dry climate.

Cecille is wearing a ring and a gold bead necklace. Her long dress is white cambric with lace on the hem and collar. Big silk bows adorn the shoulders.

Jeanette has a slightly longer gold bead necklace with a St. Christopher medal attached.

Both children are wearing black kid button shoes. Jeanette's have black bows added.

Mrs. Murphy was expecting Mildred at this time and therefore would not have appeared in a photograph. During a pregnancy women were rarely seen out of their house and were never photographed.

This blue satin dress is trimmed in white lace. The bodice is pouched over a heavily stitched waistline.

Even though this type of dress was recommended for "the small, dainty woman," a straight-fronted, fully-boned corset was nevertheless necessary to achieve right effect.

The dress was made in one piece and the soft outer fabric was sewn onto a heavy fabric that was also boned. When a woman put on a dress of this era, she became the size of the dress whatever size she wore originally. Such a dress gave the illusion of being all flowing softness when it was actually constructed along the lines of a suit of armor.

Her hat is blue velvet with ostrich feathers.

In this picture Jeanette has added the jacket and an ermine muff and neck scarf. Ermine was very admired for the contrast of its all white coat with a jet black tail.

Jeanette's slender, full-bosomed figure, her dark hair, and large, luminous dark eyes, beautifully formed mouth and hair contributed to her appearance of a woman of wealth and breeding.

The little Jeanette poses in a dancing costume at the Murphys' favorite photographers, "Stevens in the McVicker's Theatre Building."

Jeanette's dress has a butterfly on the shoulder. She is wearing shiny black boots with the latest style of "fancy foxed heel."

How sad that such a lovely child would die so young!

Mildred is riding a tricycle that was advertised in this way: "Many parents prefer them for their children by reason of safety, convenience and the ease with which they can be run by the little girl or boy."

This fancy model had rubber-tire wheels, a spring seat upholstered in plush and furnished with a back. The frame was enameled black and in 1897 it cost J.B. Murphy $11.65. This was a very expensive toy when you consider that for $11.28 one could purchase a 225-pound "Star Sun Shine Cook Stove."

Mildred's hat was a navy blue "sailor tam." She is wearing black Melton leggings, a double-breasted reefer jacket in dark red with large white pearl buttons in front.

The shoulder cape is fur and her skirt is wool plaid. A gold bracelet completes the pleasant costume.

Behind J.B.'s little Cecille and Mildred wait the top-hatted coachman, horse and carriage.

The pompous cadence of a high-stepping coach horse was in great demand among Chicago's well-to-do. Such a horse weighed 1,100-1,250 pounds and had a speed of eight to ten miles an hour.

Keeping a carriage horse in beautiful condition required the services of a fulltime groom to walk the horse until cooled down, curry-comb him, use a hoof pick to locate any offending pebbles and finally water him and put him in his stall (which the groom had cleaned while the horse was on the road). A coach horse had his own stall, a cabinet of liniments and medicine as well as a lavish supply of oats, corn, sweet hay and bedding.

Despite the cost and care of horses, they were a necessary part of the marble-top sideboard, mansard roof, red velvet draperies and ostrich-plume hat lifestyle of the wealthy of 1890.

Jeanette in this picture is the perfect Edwardian woman. She is displaying her husband's wealth on her person, therefore her dress is lavish and unfit for activity.

Such a large hat would be uncomfortable; however, the more useless and helpless a woman appeared the higher her presumed social status. A well dressed female who ventured out of doors without a hat was assumed to be emotionally distracted, mentally disturbed or of loose morals.

Tilting her head just slightly, the beautiful Jeanette clearly had a sense of personal theater and was doing her part to promote her husband and family's standing in the community.

This picture of Mrs. John B. Murphy was probably taken the year of the World's Fair in Chicago, 1893. Chicago was seen for the first time by millions of Americans who began to realize the miracle of Chicago's growth. In 1837 wolves howled in the same streets that by 1893 were principal business addresses.

Jeanette had four children at that time. Harold had died, and this year little Jeanette would follow him.

This dress is made of wool and velvet edged with fur. Her hat is circled with puffed velvet; wide bows of fancy silk ribbon are on the top.

J.B. was professor of clinical surgery at the College of Physicians and Surgeons (later the University of Illinois Medical School), and had recently startled the surgical world by the introduction of the "Murphy-button" published in his article on "Cholecysto-Intestinal, Gastro-Intestinal, Entero-Intestinal Anastomosis and Approximation Without Sutures."

Judging from Jeanette's costume this was taken in 1894. It may have been at the Washington Park Race Track, then the City's most elegant southside track.

This is an Edwardian woman at her best. Jeanette is handling hat, dress and horse with grace and style. This sort of dress required eighteen or twenty yards of material. While the hat's character is hard to see, it was likely a great pouf of silk roses, white plumes, taffeta ribbons and chiffon net.

Jeanette is carrying the whole show off as if there was nothing to it—giving no evidence of the heat and dust that certainly were there to contend with.

The two girls riding with her are too old to be Jeanette's daughters. They are dressed according to their respective ages; the younger one in short skirts and hair down, the older companion in long skirts and hair up.

The Morgan horse looks frisky, and yet Jeanette has him and the situation entirely under control.

The Venetian Building
34-36 Washington Street
between State Street and Wabash Avenue

Columbus Memorial Building
State and Washington Streets

The picture on the left features a version of the Venetian building that dwarfs its neighbor, the Columbus Memorial Building. The picture on the right is more faithful to fact. The Columbus Memorial Building was built the year of the World's Fair. It boasted a ten-foot statue of Columbus done in bronze in Rome. The globe on top was of opalescent glass with the continents marked in color with a cut jewel locating Chicago.

Next to the Columbus on Washington Street was a prestigious office address, the Venetian Building. In 1891 J.B. had come back from Colorado free of symptoms of tuberculous. The College of Physicians and Surgeons offered him a surgery professorship. J.B. moved his practice to the expensive Venetian office building and set to work on the problem of intestinal anastomosis.

HAYMARKET THEATRE
161 WEST MADISON ST.
CHICAGO

Morrison

While J.B. was making a name in surgery, it is clear from this photograph that Jeanette was devoting great attention to little Cecille. In this picture Cecille strikes a carefully practiced pose in her dancing costume.

Cecille is wearing side-button kid boots. An advertisement at the time stated that such footwear was, "genteel and dressy for fine wear."

A few years later, Cecille's dress was eyelet embroidery with satin ribbon threaded through the fabric to create a rich and complicated appearance.

The bodice is pleated from the lace yoke to the waist giving the fashionable fullness this Edwardian style called for.

The high neck and cuffs are lace and Cecille is wearing white stockings with white high-top side-button shoes of kid leather.

Adding to the richness of the scene are Cecille's two gold rings, the oriental carpet and a monstrocity of of piece of furniture that appears to be not quite a table or chair and yet somehow "both."

The girl's hairstyle is the result of a careful maid's winding Cecille's long hair into pieces of cloth which then dried into tight curls. When dry the hair was carefully worked around a finger or a comb into the ringlet fashion.

T his was the picture J.B. kept in his private office.
Displayed in an ornate silver frame, this image of J.B.'s family in 1909 held a conspicuous place on the mantlepiece.

Jeanette's beauty seemed not to diminish through the years and she had the qualities necessary to gain and keep a place in the hierarchy of great ladies which ruled Chicago society from the 1880's to the second World War. She and her daughters' clothing was decorated with elaborate trimmings, embroidery and a combination of pale fabric with elaborate hand decoration. Perfectly groomed and coiffed, they presented a gracious, royal image.

J.B. Murphy's house stood at 3305 Michigan Avenue. Such a chateauesque style was rare as it required massive masonry construction and elaborate expensive detailing. This style was used primarily in architect-designed landmark houses.

The chateauesque elements have been indicated on the picture.

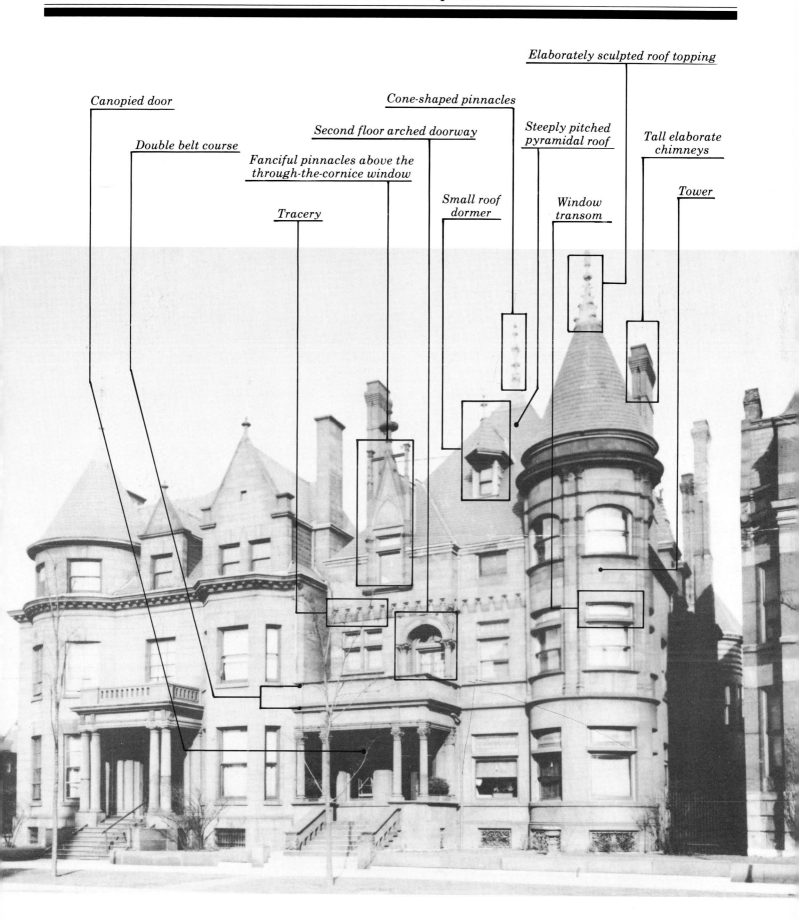

Elaborately sculpted roof topping

Canopied door

Cone-shaped pinnacles

Double belt course

Second floor arched doorway

Steeply pitched pyramidal roof

Tall elaborate chimneys

Fanciful pinnacles above the through-the-cornice window

Tracery

Small roof dormer

Window transom

Tower

The Surgeon

Here J.B. is looking every bit the successful and trust inspiring doctor. He is wearing a formal suit and white shirt with high standing collar. J.B. always reflected the height of "good dressing." His was the exact degree of correctness in dress, the cut and quality of the fabric in suits and coats, perfectly shaped hats in the best felts, the finest leathers and workmanship in boots and shoes. Shirts and ties were chosen with great care to match or tone perfectly. Gloves in soft leather and the right color were always worn or carried. J.B. had learned how much men judge from the press of a suit, or the shine of a boot.

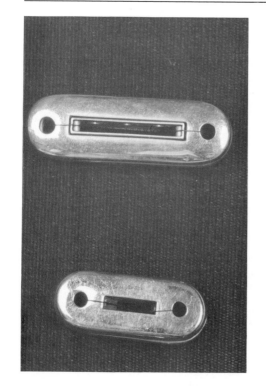

Excerpt from Dr. John Murphy's Clinics, Volume I, No. 1, February 1912.

These examples of the Murphy Buttons were donated to the Museum of Medical Progress in Prairie du Chien, Wisconsin, by C.D. Neidhold, M.D. of Appleton, Wisconsin. Once common, the Murphy Buttons have become so rare that this collection alone makes a visit to the museum a rewarding experience.

second needle. In putting in this button you catch it on the cup and then put it in. With the other you catch it on the cylinder. You cap on the cuff and get it in, then change it and take the cylinder. Here is the other half of the Hartman forceps. That is pushed down on the button below the cap. Now we are ready to make the approximation. We will take off the clamp from the jejunum, so as to allow the jejunum to come around in the position necessary, and you see the opening is closed behind with my thumb.

Now we are going to put in stitches in such a way that there will be no traction on this zone of approximation. We do the same thing when we use a suture. We take off tension from the line of fixation. You will see there has been no possibility of any type of escape of material from this zone in which we were working. You see here the advantage which the button has over the line of suture in that particular. We do probably three-fourths of our cases with the button. Occasionally, when we have two cases in a day, we do one with the suture and do the other with the button. We can do both. We like the button better than the suture because we think it requires less skill, less care, and that it is no additional hazard in any part of the gut.

You will recall the number of buttons that were not found after operations, and it was believed they were retained in the intestinal tract. In rebuilding one of the hospitals they found 21 buttons at a sewer junction, showing how perfectly regular they were in their passage.

In making this anastomosis you noticed that I made it so as to have traction in the same line of axis propelling the contents of the intestinal canal. You see, it was put up in this shape [indicating]. There was a normal relationship established between the jejunum and the stomach. In the upper zone of the abdomen it is much more important to have an ectropium of the peritoneum than it is in the lower.

In weighing the statistics with the button and the various means, particularly the suture, which is probably the only one that is lined up with it at this time, we have to consider, first, what are the dangers with any method of approximation? The dangers with any method are—first, failure of union, which, of course, is very slight with any of the methods that are in vogue at the present time; second, and more important than the danger of failure of union, is the danger of hemorrhage. The great⸺ ⸺ortality following gastro-enterostomy at the

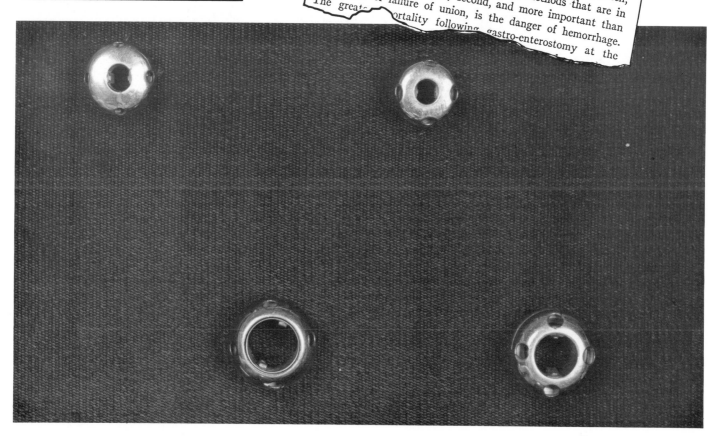

J.B. Murphy with beard.

Excerpt from
"Clinics of John B. Murphy"
Vol. 1, February 1912, No. 1

REMARKS ON COUNTING SPONGES

The interne, to whom is intrusted the recording of the counting of the sponges, has been on the service only since the first of the month. He has not had many sentences passed on him as yet. Sister Victorine counted the sponges, and she knows the number is right when the abdomen is closed. A report of the number of sponges must go on every history. By that system you are not so likely to leave sponges in the abdomen after the wound has been closed. The only wonder is that sponges are not left in the abdomen more frequently, but by having one party responsible for them, you succeed in avoiding mistakes or accidents to a greater degree than by having a haphazard method of keeping track of them. I make it a business to ask the doctor with reference to the number of sponges removed, because I am teaching all the time and it is very important to do this. If I should neglect to ask him, it is his duty to see that the record shall show the number of sponges. This lessens the liability of accidents.

When this picture was taken, abdominal operations were considered a method of the executioner by most lay people and many surgeons. However, J.B. was campaigning to convince the medical world that the malady known as perityphlitis or cholera morbus was appendicitis and should be treated by immediate appendectomy.

The women in the audience are probably nursing students, the men are students or visiting physicians.

At this time surgeons had not adopted rubber gloves or face masks. It is horrifying to think of the open wound amid the accumulation of germs generated by this large group of onlookers. Nevertheless this surgical technique was a good deal advanced from conditions when J.B. was a student and the old time surgeons operated without removing their hats.

Surgery had progressed a long way, nevertheless the application of the knife to flesh still proclaimed the master and exposed the novice. Incising, suturing, and knot tying were the grammar of surgery and everyone agreed that J.B. had a wonderful way with "words."

The clinics he held at Mercy were famous. The daily attendance averaged one hundred and fifty. As many as thirty-two states, as well as Canada and foreign countries, were represented at one time in the audience.

From March 21, 1895 until his death, J.B. was Chief Surgeon at Mercy Hospital, Chicago. While J.B. had both the will and the power to see his wishes made law, he also had the good fortune to have Sister Mary Raphael on his side. Sister recognized that what was good for Dr. Murphy was also good for Mercy Hospital. In those days the word of the Mother Superior was obeyed perfectly. This made for a very efficient working system and contributed in no small measure to J.B.'s success.

In this anesthetic technique chloroform was poured drop-by-drop on several thicknesses of gauze laid over a piece of wire netting stretched on a frame above the patient's nose.

This photo is unusual because a man is administering the anesthesia; Dr. Murphy usually made use of the dedicated services of Sister Mary Ethelreda, a member of the first class to graduate from Mercy's Nursing School. This good nun was also the first Mercy nurse to take up the study of anesthesia.

Early on in anesthesia it was wrongly believed that any one holding a can of ether or dropping chloroform was as good as anyone else. Dr. Murphy had the sense to recognize the inherent danger in unskilled anesthesia and therefore he set great stock in Sister Mary Ethelreda's capabilities.

Another important member of J.B.'s surgical team was Sister Mary Victorine. She was his surgical nurse for ten years. Sister kept a notebook that is in the Archives at Mercy Hospital. To read it is to be impressed with the attention each surgical detail was given by Sister Victorine, no doubt her skillful preparation added much to Dr. Murphy's success rate.

These tests one can make then and there in a few moments at the bedside. Then you can say to the patient and his people with a feeling of positiveness which carries conviction that you know what is the matter. Remember that when people do not accept your professional conclusions, it is not always and entirely their fault. It is the element of doubt in your own mind that betrays itself to the people through some medium of which the doctor is often not aware, an intuition, if you wish to call it that, which nature had given Man for his protection. The people recognize that you are faltering, and they hesitate or decline to follow your line of action. If you are positive in your own mind concerning your case, they will follow your advice readily and they will do just what you are convinced is the right thing to do. One often hears the stock expression used by physicians, "The people would not let me do it." It is just as often the doctor's fault as the patient's.

"You knew when he stood at the operating table that no matter what emergency came up he would be the master of it."

—Sister Mary Victorine

Excerpt from
Clinics of John B. Murphy

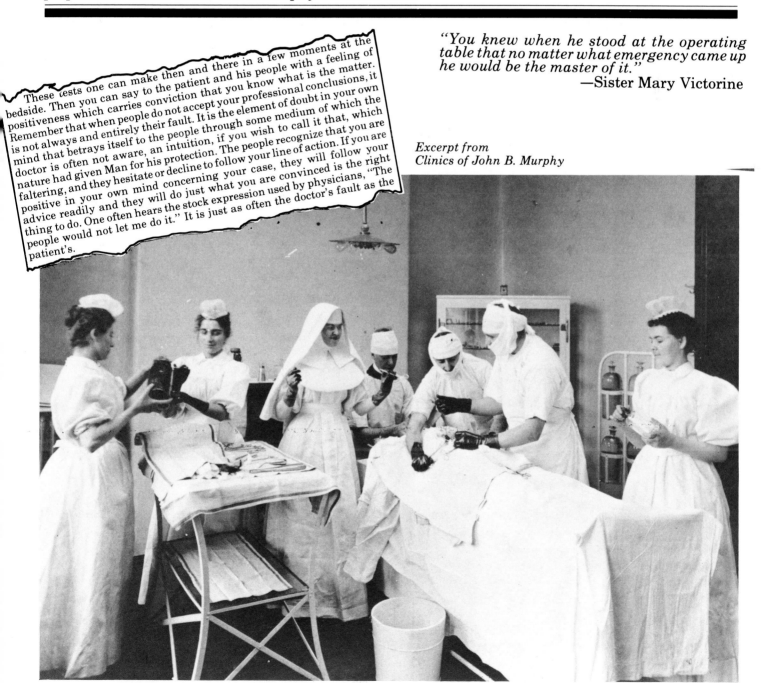

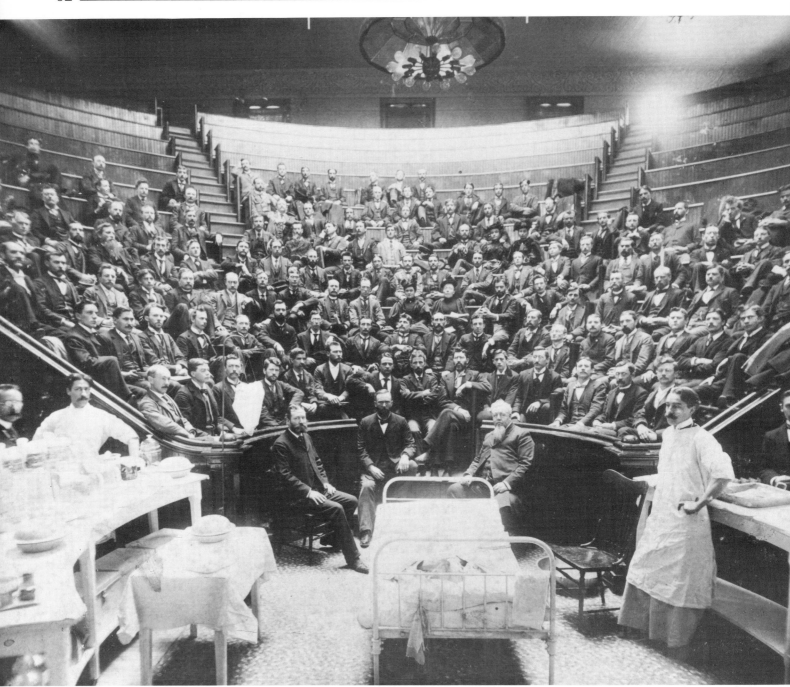

T his is a dissection scene. J.B. seated on the left, front row, and Dr. Christian Fenger on the right. Dr. Fenger had been J.B.'s early teacher; he believed that all medical knowledge began at the dissection table.

The empty containers and the jars of alcohol and ether are available for the tissue and organ specimens.

The elaborate lamp is made of early incandescent bulbs and a mirror reflector. This lamp was very up-to-date, as Thomas Edison's success with his carbonized cotton filament sealed in a glass globe occurred in 1879 and this photo was taken in 1896.

Cook County was also abreast of its time in the attitude they held toward the value of dissection in order to understand the course of disease.

Dr. Murphy and Dr. Fenger first met when J.B. was a student and Dr. Fenger was on the staff at Cook County giving lectures and demonstrations in pathological anatomy.

By 1896 Dr. Murphy and Dr. Fenger were both on the staff at Mercy Hospital.

In 1896 J.B. had gained a reputation with the "Murphy Button" in intestinal surgery and his work in appendicitis. Also in 1896, J.B. invaded the nervous system at a time when this branch of surgery had hardly been touched. He astonished the medical world when he operated on a patient for a fibrous tumor of the uterus, removed the tumor, repaired the incision and did not disturb the fetus.

In the Home Encyclopedia of Health *published in 1901, note the "cures" offered for appendicitis.*

Erysipelas.—Boil white navy beans, mash and add cornmeal to make poultice. Apply hot and change frequently.

Indigestion.—An exclusive diet of fruit for several days is found efficacious in most cases of indigestion. This diet is excellent in dyspepsia and constipation.

Insomnia.—On going to bed, take some sound, as a clock-tick or the breathing of some one within hearing, and breathe long full breaths, keeping time to the sound. In a very short time you will fall asleep, without any of the painful anxieties attending insomnia.

Croup.—Fat bacon applied to the throat, as in sore throat, is recommended as a remedy for croup. Its action can be helped by taking internally a few drops of kerosene oil on sugar.

Nervous Headache.—A cloth wet with spirits of camphor and sprinkled with black pepper when applied to the head, gives relief.

Appendicitis.—To allay the pain and stop the formation of pus in appendicitis it is recommended that a flannel cloth be saturated with hot water, wring it out, drop ten to fifteen drops of turpentine upon it and apply it to the afflicted parts as hot as the patient can bear. Repeat till relief is obtained. Then cover the bowels with a thin cotton cloth, upon which place another cloth wrung out of kerosene oil. This sustains the relief and conduces to rest and eventual cure. It is an essential part of the absorbent cure for appendicitis, and since its adoption doctors do not resort to a surgical operation half so often. A liver pill should be used and taken every few nights at bed-time.

2. Dr. Wm. W. Myers says that root of wild yam is a good remedy for appendicitis; one ounce to a pint of water, boiled down to a half-pint. Take a teaspoonful every hour until relieved, and then every two hours until cured.

Neuralgic.—Make a t... the root of twin leaf and...

the nose; there is danger of nose-bleed and the patient is unable to swallow.

VISITING PHYSICIAN: Doctor, what is your opinion of nitrous oxid gas as an anesthetic?

DR. MURPHY: We use it quite a little. Of course, ether is our favorite anesthetic here. Whenever we have an intestinal obstruction; whenever we have any desire to have the patient come out immediately from under the anesthesia; wherever we do a minor operation—we use nitrous oxid oxygen. We start every case with nitrous oxid oxygen. The minor operations we carry through with it, if we desire. But our anesthetic here is ether. It has been very satisfactory to us, and I think the reason is that we have had one party giving it for many years, and that that party is not a doctor, but a religeuse, which is a very great advantage in giving an anesthetic. The Sister sees the patient the night before the operation; she sees to the preparation of the patient, looks after the urine examination, sprays the throat, gives orders for and looks after the patient after the operation. Her opinion as to the patient's condition is more valuable to me than that of any one else.

VISITING PHYSICIAN: What about nerve block?

DR. MURPHY: We do not use it. In Europe this summer I ... all that variety of anesthesia and saw the various methods ... If y...

Excerpt from Dr. John B. Murphy Clinics, Volume I, No. 2-6.

On October 14, 1912 in Milwaukee as ex-President Theodore Roosevelt was leaving the Gilpatrick Hotel to make a campaign speech he was shot by an insane fanatic. His life was saved because earlier he had put his folded speech manuscript and a steel spectacle case in his breast pocket. This action saved his life, for the bullet's power was reduced somewhat by going through the papers and the steel case.

After the shooting, Roosevelt went on to make the intended speech and only when that was accomplished did he allow his friends to suggest he see a doctor. Recognizing J.B. Murphy's name, Roosevelt left immediately for Chicago by train. When J.B. came aboard, he found Roosevelt ignoring his injury and walking around as if nothing unusual had happened. Fixing Colonel Roosevelt with a look not unlike the one in this photo, Dr. Murphy commanded and the Colonel obeyed. Roosevelt went to Mercy Hospital to bed and was resigned to obey his doctor's orders.

The world called for the bullet's removal, but J.B. stood firmly in his conviction that only infection would be gained by trying to retrieve the bullet. Roosevelt lived in great health until endocarditis felled him in 1919, the bullet still in place.

Nineteen thirteen saw J.B. in company with Dr. Harvey Cushing, Dr. William Mayo and Dr. George Crile, all of America, being installed as fellows of the Royal College of Surgeons of England. These doctors and their signatures are reproduced here.

Also forever immortalized is an unnamed youth who chose the picture-taking moment to fold his arms and rest on a convenient window seat nearby.

Walking sticks, hats, gloves and tie pins were apparel items that gentlemen often had about them. In this photo J.B. is the only one to display all the possibilities. He was not going to let the Englishmen suspect that an American from the Midwest would not know how to dress properly.

When this picture was taken Dr. Murphy was chief of the surgical staff of Mercy Hospital, a staff member of Alexian Brothers Hospital, attending surgeon to Cook County Hospital, consulting surgeon to St. Joseph's and Columbus Memorial Hospitals, and the Hospital for Crippled Children, Chicago.

Recipients of Honorary Degree of Fellowship of the Royal College of Surgeons of England Aug. 6. 1913.

The Sister has to give the anesthetic in this case through the nose; there is danger of nose-bleed and the patient is unable to swallow.

VISITING PHYSICIAN: Doctor, what is your opinion of nitrous oxid gas as an anesthetic?

DR. MURPHY: We use it quite a little. Of course, ether is our favorite anesthetic here. Whenever we have an intestinal obstruction; whenever we have any desire to have the patient come out immediately from under the anesthesia; wherever we do a minor operation—we use nitrous oxid oxygen. We start every case with nitrous oxid oxygen. The minor operations we carry through with it, if we desire. But our anesthetic here is ether. It has been very satisfactory to us, and I think the reason is that we have had one party giving it for many years, and that that party is not a doctor, but a religeuse, which is a very great advantage in giving an anesthetic. The Sister sees the patient the night before the operation; she sees to the prepara- tion of the patient, looks after the urine examination, sprays the throat, gives orders for and looks after the patient after the operation. Her opinion as to the patient's condition is more valuable to me than that of any one else.

VISITING PHYSICIAN: What about nerve block?

DR. MURPHY: We do not use it. In Europe this summer I saw all that variety of anesthesia and saw the various methods used splendidly. If you ask me now, after seeing all that, if I had to have an operation on my knee-joint would I take local

*Excerpt from
Dr. John B. Murphy's
Clinics, Volume I,
Nos. 2-6*

Here Dr. Murphy is preparing to apply his skill to the right hand of a black patient who unfor- tunately had caught his hand in a machine that pulled most of the epi- dermis toward the fingers.

Dr. Murphy's assistants have ligated the bleeding vessel and pre- pared the area. J.B. will now attempt to reconnect the severed tendons so that the fingers will not be useless. J.B. is wearing an early type of head lamp used to direct light intensely upon the injury.

Will and Charlie Mayo met Murphy when they went to Chicago to watch and learn from J.B.'s teacher, Christian Fenger. The Mayos taught J.B. the repair of umbilical hernia and the brothers learned about the Murphy Button in Chicago from J.B. himself.

Summers found the Mayos at their cottage on Lake Allis near Oronoco. They drove back and forth to Rochester every day. On weekends they often cruised down the Mississippi with a party of professional friends. In this photo taken on June 15, 1915 J.B. and Will Mayo relax on the comfortable pleasure craft.

Will and Charlie Mayo's admiration for J.B. was unbounded and unconcealed. They considered him one of the greatest surgeons of his generation anywhere and expressed this opinion at the dedication of the Murphy Memorial.

Comments from his *Clinics:*
"The wound is now closed with horsehair and without damage and sealed with cotton and collodin."

"Men have not the capacity to endure pain which many women have."

"Procrastination and conservation are the synonyms of inefficiency and cowardice."

Library and lounging room.

"Today is the day of salvation for an acute appendicitis—Operate."

"The surest way to beat the man who critizes you unfairly is to do him a good turn."

"We do not like to operate on such fat patients, there is too much blubber in the way. It was a question with her whether we should cut or blast, she had so much fat."

"When his eyes began to shine you knew he had a big idea and that something important was going to come up."
—Sister Mary Victorine

Library and lounging room.

In his clinics J.B. mentions that, *"One 'cure' for T.B. called the 'walking fad' had patients walking barefooted in wet grass and climbing mountains before breakfast."* Naturally J.B. was not impressed with this.

Another waiting and resting room.

More J.B. quotes:

"Interpreting signs and symptoms into pathologic entities is the most difficult proposition in medicine."

"If the patient wants perfect locomotion guaranteed, he should spend his money on an automobile."

Ladies waiting room.

"The doing of the operation is a matter of minor importance which you can soon learn on the cadaver and the animal. The diagnosis is of major importance and can be acquired only at the bedside area with the patient present."

Dr. Richard J. Tivnen's private office and examining room. Dr. Tivnen was head of Eye, Ear, Nose and Throat department.

Dr. George W. Hochrein's office.

"Remember the patient is the unit around which all your life must revolve—scientific, moral, social, and otherwise. Your obligation always comes back to the individual patient. That is the purpose for which you study medicine, to benefit the patient."

"Sister Victorine is responsible for the sponges and the intern is responsible for putting it on the record."

Waiting room for patients of Drs. Richard J. Tivnen and Charles L. Mix.

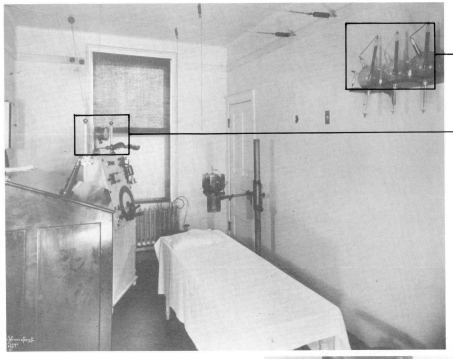

Replacements

Lightning rods

X-ray room with open x-ray and open non-vacuum tube.

"Sister reports the sponge, counted and correct."

"Like death it is the after-effects, not the procedure itself, of which we are afraid."
J.B. talking about a surgical case.

Filing room for the x-ray plates.

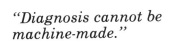

"Diagnosis cannot be machine-made."

"The doctor who waits before diagnosing will pass the undertaker on the patient's doorstep."

Examining and dressing room.

From the *Victorian Almanac,* a book of medical home care we read:

In 1856 the advice to remedy apoplexy was "immediate and large bleeding from the arm, cupping at the back of the neck, leaches to the temples . . . one or two drops of croton oil rubbed or dropped on the tongue.

Mediocology 1901 Illustrated of 1901 advises: "blood may be taken, carefully, from the arm or by cups or leeches applied to the back of the neck," to reduce "hysteria."

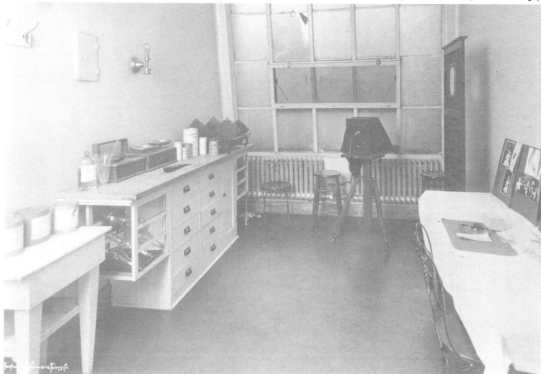

More of J.B.'s sayings:

"The patient's interest takes precedence over all other things."

Laboratory Room No. 1

Photographic studio where cases are photographed.

"There is always a why for the wherefore, if you hunt hard enough for it."

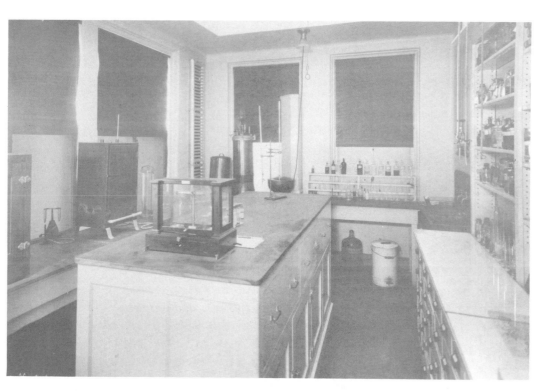

In 1901 the book *Home Care* offered advice for treating appendicitis, "assume a position where the abdominal muscles will be as much relaxed as possible. Avoid sneezing, coughing, and so forth. The diet should at first consist of only small quantities of cold or lukewarm milk, oatmeal, boullion from white meat, and so forth.

Scarlet Fever: "the external use of fat and raw bacon is highly recommended."

Diptheria: "a free application of petroleum well rubbed in at the throat frequently cures diptheria. Blow pulverized taimen upon the tonsils to destroy the germs of diptheria."

Travels

received came to Doctor Murphy in June 1919 from His Holiness, Pope Benedict XV—"the Christian Knighthood and the apostolic blessing"—an honor which was conferred upon him in recognition of his exceptional services to humanity and of his many works of Christian charity.

Those who attended the Los Angeles session of the Association in 1911 were impressed by the scholarly address, handsome appearance and charm of personality. When he received at the President's reception, with his beautiful wife and two charming daughters, it formed a picture to be remembered.

It is distinctly unfortunate that Doctor Murphy did not train

J.B. became president of the American Medical Association in June, 1911 at Los Angeles, California. He spoke on "Organized Medicine, It's Influence and It's Obligations."

J.B. and his family took advantage of being in California and toured extensively. In this picture they have driven from Los Angeles to Santa Barbara on dirt roads, a distance of more than 100 miles. However, this was only the beginning: The brave little band continued on to Crater Lake and Medford, Oregon.

Even while braving these unpaved roads, Jeanette and her friends wore the huge plumed and beribboned hats of the period.

Notice that all of these women have lace on their dresses and that their skirts are each draped in a different style.

Carrying a purse was a mark of fashion as well as a necessity now that face powder had become popular.

The umbrella was for sun protection—an alabaster complexion was still a lady's goal in 1911.

Here is proof that traveling in pairs was a sensible idea in 1911. When one of the Pierce-Arrows found the going a bit muddy, the other one came to the rescue.

For the trip through California and Oregon the Murphy famiy and friends rode in Pierce-Arrow cars which were second to none in pleasing the highly developed tastes of the wealthy.

The pictured cars were 48 h.p. 6-cylinder touring cars that cost $7,000 in 1911. They boasted Morocco leather upholstery, thick velour carpets, engines that had been listened to by skilled fitters with stethoscopes before being approved for sale. Another unusual feature was the steering wheel on the right side of the car.

T hese photos show the visitors boarding the train for Culebra Cut.

When Dr. Murphy visited the site of excavation in the Culebra Cut, its environs had reached the staggering total of 150 million cubic yards; nineteen million pounds of dynamite had been exploded in the Cut; six and a half thousand men streamed each day into the Cut working ten hour shifts in temperatures up to 120 degrees Fahrenheit.

When the day laborers quit the Cut by night it was the beginning of labor for the four to five hundred who worked as machine repairmen, coal loaders and track repair squads. The night was spent preparing for the day.

The motto of the Canal Zone was, "The Land Divided, the World United."

For seven years Culebra Cut was never silent, not even for an hour.

If all the material from the canal were placed in one solid shaft with a base the dimension of a city block, it would tower nineteen miles into the air.

Few visitors were permitted to visit the work down in the Cut. It is a mark of the importance of this group that they were allowed to ride on the 76 miles of construction track within the nine mile canyon.

Alice Roosevelt Longworth toured the canal and shocked everybody by smoking in public.

Culebra Cut

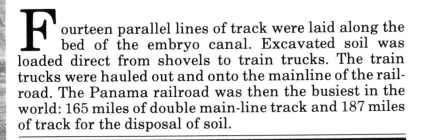

ourteen parallel lines of track were laid along the bed of the embryo canal. Excavated soil was loaded direct from shovels to train trucks. The train trucks were hauled out and onto the mainline of the railroad. The Panama railroad was then the busiest in the world: 165 miles of double main-line track and 187 miles of track for the disposal of soil.

Steam shovels did 90 percent of the dry excavation. First the area was drilled and blasted with gunpowder. Next two lines of parallel railway track was laid alongside the debris; steam shovels were then hauled into position along the lower track and dump cars along the upper. The shovels would grub up debris and swing it directly into the dump cars. As soon as the cars were full, they were hauled away and replaced by another. Repair work was done at night by a roving work party.

A jaunty young man sits on a portion of the lock wall. When finished, these walls were one thousand feet long and rose higher than a six-story building.

The houses in this picture were family homes in which the officials of the Canal Project lived. All houses were furnished by the government, coal was provided for cooking and ice for the iceboxes. There were no electric light bills, no water bills and no drugstore accounts to meet. Free medical attention was provided.

In the war against mosquitos it was necessary to keep down grass and brush, to provide free flowing drainage ditches and to have all windows and doors screened. Consequently the pursuit for "sanitary living conditions" produced a neat and visually pleasing compound for the workers, their wives and children.

Left to right is Dr. Murphy, Major General Goethals and Dr. Gorgas.
George Washington Goethals was a Major General in the U.S. Army in charge of the Panama Canal construction project. He carried the project to practical completion without setback or delay. When this picture was taken Goethals was a hero and the long sought success was at hand.

Dr. William Crawford Gorgas, a surgeon in the U.S. Army was responsible for instituting and overseeing the practices that rid the canal of the mosquito and thereby malaria and yellow fever. He was the world's master of tropical sanitation.

In this photo we see three benefactors of mankind.

Two cultures look into the camera from either side of a patient oxen.
Mr. Hurley on the left represents the businessman of Chicago, 1912: on the right is the oxen's owner, also a businessman. Both men are hatted and carry canes, wear vests and white shirts. Each is capable in his own world and a stranger to that of the other.

August, 1912 found J.B., Cecille, Mildred and Ethel Amberg sailing on the *Mauritania*. Here diversions to combat ennui were possible on the hundreds of feet of deck space. With no radio, movies or T.V. to keep passengers inside, the young people especially found entertainment in "shipboard flirtations."

The *Mauritania* was J.B.'s favorite cruise ship. Here was prestige, glamour, a first-class lounge with classical columns and a glass dome. The main dining room was two decks high with a sunken center well. This photo was taken on the first class starboard deck: The men are wearing the new "touring or golf" cap.

The young man with a camera and white pants is wearing a "Norfolk" jacket which had come in vogue for "automobile travel, bike riding, and country outings." Presumably this fellow is flaunting it on shipboard to suggest a sportsman's image to any ladies he might encounter.

His companion is dressed far more conservatively in a dark suit and wing tip collar—also an image calculated to impress the ladies.

Ethel's two piece loose outfit was usually reserved for "country wear activities." The overall effect gave a generally "nononsense" attitude toward life.

Mildred has the new comfortable jacket and the straight-off-the-ground skirt with an added touch of luxury in the embroidered collar and pockets.

Cecille's shapeless, long, easy fitting coat was the last word in current fashion. It was lined in crepe-de chine and fastened at the left front, low-on-the-hip with enormous buttons. All three are wearing white boots with covered wood French heels. Mildred's have patent leather added. Such a boot cost $8.00 and was sold in 1912 in sizes 2½ to 8.

The Leisure Life

Jeanette is wearing a dress that would have been appropriate at the French Court at Versailles. Even with this costume ballgown Jeanette is wearing her favorite string of pearls.

This photo was taken at the "Bernard La Marche Studio, 307 Fine Arts Building, 203 Michigan Avenue, Chicago."

Handsome of bearing, with a fine thoughtful face, mustache, blue eyes, with an almost exaggerated refinement of courtesy, J.B. was the very pattern of a gentleman. He had the power to convey an air of truth and confidence to his anxious patients and the decorum suited to distressing circumstances.

J.B. wore gray, navy, beige, tan and white. His appearance suggested a general attitude of seriousness, hard work, propriety and status. The stripes he chose seem to reflect his organized effort and the ability to follow the line he had laid out for himself. Thus his clothes suggested his dependability and rectitude. This type of discreet buttoned-up look distinguished the proper gentleman of 1913.

This charming Boston Bull dog was a gift to Mildred from her uncle, Charles Plamondon. "Tinker Bell" won J.B.'s heart (and thereby a life of luxury) by responding perfectly to J.B.'s requests for tricks.

Charles Plamondon and his wife sailed to Europe on the queen of the Cunard fleet, the *Lusitania*. Leaving on Saturday morning, May 1, 1915, they shared First-Class with a microcosm of America's well-known, and well-shod.

The weather was perfect and the sea, smooth. For six soft days the passengers enjoyed the most luxurious liner afloat.

On May 7th, within sight of land, a heavy muffled sound and a tremor throughout the ship signaled disaster: Of the 1,924 aboard only 726 were saved.

The Lusitania had been torpedoed by "Unterseeboot-20"; thus war between America and Germany became inevitable.

Charles and his wife were among the dead.

In just three months from this March fishing scene Archduke Francis Ferdinand, heir to the Austrian throne, and his wife were assassinated in Sarajevo on June 28, 1914. However, all was serene as Mildred and Ethel tried fishing on the Atlantic Ocean. Even while fishing, the men have three-piece suits, ties and hats; the women contend with dresses, scarfs, veils, hats and white gloves.

An accepted fact in 1914 was that the sort of clothes one wore expressed the values of society; fashion projected identity and gave outward form and meaning to inner values. Therefore comfort and utility were rarely consulted when one decided what to wear.

The Wright brothers in 1903 produced the world's first powered man-carrying airplane. Flying science improved so rapidly that by 1914 planes had been built that could fly at speeds of over 125 miles per hour, reach altitudes of 25,000 feet and fly non-stop for more than a thousand miles.

Nevertheless, the sight of a flying machine overhead was still enough reason to aim the Kodak upward.

Flying over the Murphy fishing party was a Curtiss plane. The inventor, Glenn Curtiss, built a plane in 1907 that he named "June Bug." In 1908 Glenn won the *Scientific American's* prize for the first public flight in America of over one kilometer. He continued to win prizes for his ever improving planes and in 1911 he launched his first practical hydroplane. The first two planes the U.S. government ordered were from Glenn Curtiss.

J eanette with a fox "choker scarf" and a dress that proves one could be fashionable yet not a slave to fashion (Jeanette continued to wear flattering form-fitting dresses during the height of the shapeless dress era.)

She is carrying the popular handbag. It had become necessary because while the flowing Edwardian fashions could conceal essential pockets, the new narrow styles would reveal every bulge.

This type of dress was suitable for dressy afternoon occasions and less formal evening functions.

A hat such as Jeanette's was described in an advertisement of the time, "large sailor, made of silk-faced velvet, underbrim of good quality satin. The shape is becoming to both young and mature women."

Her unidentified companion sports an open-weave straw hat, called a skimmer; a dark blue serge sack suit; and a starched high collar.

In March of 1914, Dr. and Mrs. Murphy and Mildred visited Palm Beach.

On the yacht Mrs. Murphy, Mildred and their female companion are wearing the latest fashions: The silhouette of clothes was softening: They were easier looking and less contrived. Mildred's ensemble was a simple straight skirt with a straight loose jacket and a matching blouse. Her hairstyle had side curls pulled toward the face known as "kiss curls."

With an upswept coiffure Mrs. Murphy is wearing an expertly tailored suit and a beribboned hat and she is carrying a parasol. Her blouse is a softened version of the high collar worn by the Gibson Girl. Presumably the lady in white skirt and blue jacket is the yacht's owner as such a blue and white outfit was highly recommended for "genteel yachting."

J.B.'s health was not good because of plaques of calcification in his arteries which caused him to suffer angina pectoris. A doctor at the time described the condition, "the feeling of a vise-like constriction to the chest and a peculiar sense of dread, as if the last moment were come." Nevertheless J.B. gathered up his strength and looked the picture of health for these photographs.

Trout Lake, Wisconsin is the setting for this display of 1914 swimwear. Mildred and a muscled gentleman sit on a decidely makeshift perch. No doubt this photo has long survived the pier.

Mildred's suit is made up of a chemise top and knickers; a V-design at the neck contrasts with the black bathing dress.

The knickers have a wide band which covers the knees. Canvas slippers, black stockings and a swimming cap complete the swimming suit ensemble of 1914.

Mildred, her mother and Celeste were staying at Trout Lake while J.B. was in Liverpool.

Cecille had recently been married.

J.B., on the left, leans against the rail of the *Lusitania* on July 15, 1914. He is bound for Liverpool to watch Dr. Robert Jones perform a special type of surgery. Then J.B. went to Leeds to visit Sir Berkeley Monihan and to London for the Clinical Congress of Surgeons.

Declaration of war found 1100 American doctors stranded in Europe, J.B. returned on the *Mauritania* on August 9, 1914. He then organized from the staff of Mercy Hospital in Chicago, a medical unit for service with the British Expeditionary Forces.

(From Photo by Prebensen.)
View on Water Power, Showing Badger Paper Mill of Kimberly & Clark Company.

F. J. HEALY LUMBER CO.

Wholesale and Retail Pine and Hardwood Lumber, Etc.

The F. J. Healy Lumber Co. has experienced an unusually prosperous year and materially increased sales over preceding years, a fact no doubt due as much to the sterling reliability of the concern as in all lines. The company carries a complete stock of building lumber and other material of a like character and are at all times prepared to cater to parties in a most satisfactory manner, both in quality of goods and lowness of price.

J. H. Healy, manager of the concern, is one of the best known men in this section, and that he thoroughly comprehends every detail of the lumber business evidenced in the fact that he may almost be said to have been reared in a lumber yard, having had charge of an extensive lumber business long before attaining his majority. Mr. Healy went to South Dakota in 1881, where for seven years he was prominently identified with the same business, being at the same time honored with a number of public offices. He returned here in 1888, and prospered until the panic of 1893, when like thousands of others, he was seriously hurt financially. However, Mr. Healy at once set about paying his creditors, for he valued a good name more than riches, and all who knew him will read with pleasure that he is meeting with unmeasured success.

Aside from the lumber business Mr. Healy represents throughout the Fox River Valley for the Manhattan Life Insurance Co., of New York, one of the strongest and most representative insurance companies in existence.

Last spring Mr. Healy was elected superintendent of the city schools, a position he has filled to the satisfaction of all concerned.

In short, Mr. Healy is one of Neenah's best known and most highly respected citizens and most deserving of the good fortune that seems to be coming his way of late.

THE WING COMPANY.

Largest and Most Important Insurance Agency in the Fox River Valley.

That the Wing company is one of the most conspicuous fire insurance agencies in this part of the State is shown in the fact that they represent such an exceptionally long list of time-tried companies as the following: Ætna, American of Philadelphia, British American, Connecticut, English-American Fire Association, German American, Home, North America, L. & L. & G., Law Union & Crown, Lancashire, National, Niagara, N. Y. Underwriters, Northern, North British, North German, Phœnix, of London, Philadelphia Underwriters, Svea, Trans-Atlantic, Union of England, Westchester, Scottish Un. & Nat., Hamburg Underwriters, Hartford, Hanover, Imperial, Milwaukee Mechanics, Norwich Union, Palatine, Phenix Sun of New Orleans, Thuringia and others equally strong and well-known. They are therefore prepared to offer patrons every possible protection. The Wing company is officered by some of Neenah's best known people, J. A. Kimberly, jr., being president, W. A. Yule, vice-president, and W. C. Wing, secretary and Treasurer. Mr. Wing, who is a most progressive and successful business man, was born in Neenah in 1876, and shortly after attaining his majority began an active business life. He has a bright future before him.

J. HANSON & CO.

An Extensive Wholesaler of Cheese, Butter, Eggs, Etc.

While this firm has only been in business about two years, yet it has in so short a time built up a very large trade throughout the northwest, selling to the trade only excellent qualities of Wisconsin cheese, butter, eggs, etc. Mr. Hanson has had long experience in this particular business, having been for ten years connected with the firm of N. Simon & Co. He has been a resident of Neenah for 15 years or more, and bears an excellent reputation as a successful business man.

WM. SCHUMANN.

A Reliable Dealer in Buggies, Farm Machinery, Threshers, Etc.

... Neenah's oldest and best known citizens is Wm. Schumann, who has been a resident here for about 33 years. For more than a quarter century Mr. Schumann conducted a general blacksmith business, and during the latter part of that period handled buggies, wagons, farming implements, threshers, etc., devoting his entire time to the latter business for the past five years. He has been a successful man, having built up a large trade in his present line. His long experience enables him to make his pick from among the best known goods on the market. His son, Charles J. Schumann, who was born and reared in Neenah, is the active manager of the concern, and as he is an enterprising man is steadily growing.

MANUFACTURERS' NATIONAL BANK.

A Financial Institution Much Favored by The Public.

Ever since its inception, the Manufacturers' National Bank of this city has been looked upon by the general public of this community with the most marked favor by reason of the fact that the institution had been founded by men of known responsibility, men whose honor and integrity were more to them than the mere matter of gain. But a short time, therefore, lapsed before the bank had been established upon a sound footing, not so much because of the $65,000 capital stock having been paid in but equally on account of the decided confidence the people had in its promoters. And the result today is that the Manufacturers' National is one of the prominent banking houses of this section of the state. Its officers and directors are men of the most careful and conservative character, and no matter of importance is taken up without the most extended investigation and consideration. Hence all who have any dealings with the Manufacturers' National always feel safe. A general banking business is carried on.

The bank is officered by Hiram Smith as president; D. C. VanOstrand, vice president; F. C. Shattuck, second vice president; S. B. Morgan, cashier, who, together with Wm. Kellett, M. Bilistein, S. M. Hay, Charles Scheiber and D. W. Barnes, constitute the board of directors, Cashier Morgan being the exception as a director. All these gentlemen have long been representative business men of this community. President Smith has been a prominent resident of Neenah since 1854, and has always been identified with the best interests of the city. He is a native of Otsego county, New York, having been born in September, 1829. He was among the first to grasp the importance of Neenah's future, and that he reckoned well in those early days is clearly shown in the presence of the substantial city Neenah is today.

Vice president, D. C. VanOstrand, too, is a native of New York state, having been born in Syracuse in 1827. He came to Neenah in 1850, nearly half a century ago, when little other than "natural advantages" was in sight. Shortly after the coming of Hiram Smith, four years later, the two young men joined hands in business, and those hands have not been unclasped in this sense to this day. They opened a general store in 1855 and 10 years later operated the first paper mill here. They were also at one time owners of the store foundry now being conducted by Bergstrom Bros. & Co. In all these enterprises Messrs. Smith and VanOstrand were successful. The latter, unlike his partner, occasionally bowed to the urgent wishes of his friends, and from time to time held public office. He was president of the village of Neenah before it was incorporated as a city and was also a member of the State Legislature in 1865.

Second Vice-president Shattuck has been for years a member of the Kimberly-Clark Co., and is now secretary of that great paper making concern.

S. B. Morgan is a native of Alburg Springs, Vermont. He was for a number of years, 10 or more, connected with the banking business of St. Albans, in that state, and came to Neenah in 1884 to accept his present position, a place he has filled to the utmost satisfaction of all concerned since his coming. Mr. Morgan possesses the happy faculty of making and retaining fast friendships by his suavity of manner and his geniality of character.

NEENAH COLD STORAGE CO.

A Comparatively New Concern of the City.

Although having been established less than a year ago, the Neenah Cold Storage Co. has made for itself a most enviable reputation among the trade it so admirably represents, a fact no doubt due to the substantially and absolute reliability of its men who compose the company, all the business relations with the public bearing the most positive stamp of liberality and fairness. The company was organized in December of last year, being incorporated under the laws of Wisconsin and capitalized at $12,000. They absorbed the warehouse firm of N. Simon & Co. and at once began remodeling and enlarging their plant, which is located in immediate juxtaposition with the Wisconsin Centrall main passenger depot and tracks in this city. The building, part of which is two-stories and part four-stories high, was raised 16 feet and 40 feet added to the rear, thus giving them a substantial brick plant 30x150 feet, with a capacity of 50 car loads of goods. They operate what is known as the Dexter system of cold storage, than which there is nothing better on the market. The company's principal business is devoted to wholesaling butter, eggs, cheese, fruit and honey, although they handle all kinds of country produce and are prepared to pay the highest market quotations on a spot cash basis. This is a grand thing for the farmers of this section, who are thus assured a good price for all their product along this line. The company also handles large quantities of goods on commission and are extensive dealers in cheese factory and creamery supplies, egg cases, cheese boxes, paper, etc. In a word, it is a complete cold storage plant, operated along modern and progressive business lines, and The News is pleased to note that the company is meeting with most marked success.

The Neenah Cold Storage company is officered by A. D. Eldridge as president; C. S. Briggs as treasurer, and E. M. Eldridge as secretary. President Eldridge is one of the oldest and most highly respected citizens of Neenah, having had large business interests in the twin cities for many years. The fact is, he was born and reared in this community, and all his life has been as an open book. So long as he remains at the head of the Neenah Cold Storage Co. so long will that important industry continue to grow and prosper and hold the respect and confidence of sellers and buyers alike. C. S. Briggs, treasurer of the company, is one of the city's best known and most highly respected citizens and has long been a leading man, with a reputation for sterling worth and the most positive reliability.

W. C. DUNN, D. D. S.

The Doctor Has Met With a Most Flattering Reception in Neenah.

Although Dr. Dunn has been a resident of Neenah since July of the present year, yet he seems to have most thoroughly established himself even in so short a time. But there are reasons for this, good and sufficient—hence little cause for comment. In the first place, the Doctor came among us well recommended, from his old home in Elroy, where he had successfully practiced for seven years. This, together with the fact that he is very learned and much experienced in latter-day dentistry, and possessed of a most pleasing personality, soon ingratiated him into the well wishes of Neenah people, who have bestowed upon him a most cordial welcome and consequent large and growing practice. There is nothing new in dentistry worthy of adoption that the Doctor is not quick to accept for the benefit of his patrons, and his office over the National bank is most happily prepared to cater to his patrons. He is a graduate of the Chicago College of Dentistry (class of '92). Born in Wonewoc Village, Juneau county, in 1867, he followed the usual pursuits of boys until an insane idea entered his head to become a printer. He then lost caste for awhile, until about 1887, when he took up the study of dentistry, after which he once more became a useful citizen, with the result that to-day he is enjoying life, with an estimable wife, two bright boys and a lucrative practice in an honorable profession.

HOME-TRADE SHOE CO.

A Popular Place for People who Want Reliable Footwear.

A distinctively later-day merchant of Neenah is C. P. Lindsley, the active head of the Home-Trade Shoe Co., located in the two story brick building at 105 west Wisconsin avenue, where is carried a stock of fine and medium grade footwear second to none in this section. Mr. Lindsley is a thorough shoe man, with ample experience, having begun the business immediately upon leaving school, in the shoe store of C. W. Seaver, and afterward selling goods on the road three years for the great shoe manufacturing concern of Pingree & Smith, of Detroit Mich., at the head of the most talked-of men in the country, Hon. Hazen S. Pingree, the reform governor of Michigan.

Mr. Lindsley's store is a model of neatness and systematic arrangement of stock, everything about the place presenting a most pleasing appearance. There is a place for everything and everything's in its place, so that patrons are assured rapid and satisfactory service. Mr. Lindsley is conceded by manufacturers to be a sharp buyer. It is easy to conceive, therefore, that he secures the best and most fashionable as well as serviceable and comfortable footwear made. These he offers his patrons at a most profit price. The Home-Trade Co.'s Shoe store is a credit to the business houses of Neenah, and that it is meeting with success is shown in the unusually large trade they have acquired since opening here August 25, 1898.

Mr. Lindsley was born, reared and schooled in Neenah, and his many friends will read with pleasure that his business is most satisfactory.

TWIN CITY CREAMERY CO.

An Industry having a Capacity of 15,000 Pounds of Milk Per Day.

A business that of much importance to this community especially to farmers, is that of the Twin City Creamery Co., the factory being located at 302 Commercial street. The plant has a capacity for handling about 15000 pounds of milk per day, from which may be judged a large business is done. They pay our farmers the highest possible price for all milk and cream delivered to them and thus foster a very profitable industry. The present officers of the company are A. H. Hinman president E. A. Hurston, secretary and treasurer, although it is quite probable the latter will in a few days be succeeded by P. J. Roblee, who will bring to the business an experience of about 10 years in cheese making and four years in handling butter. Mr. Roblee is a native of this county, having been born in 1869 and his active connection with the creamery company will materially aid in its success.

E. A. HURSTON.

An Expert Machinist with More Than a Local Reputation.

Mr. Thurston acknowledged one of the most accomplished workmen in his line in this section of the State, as is evidenced by the calls made upon him from various cities in the surrounding territory. Mr. Thurston has made engine work a study nearly all his life and previous to establishing his business in this city five years ago had been engaged in the same line about 15 years. He is a student in this particular direction, and when he undertakes a job thoroughly comprehends what is to be done, he makes a specialty of drafting designs for all kinds of machinery, in which art he is an expert, as well as in that of indicating engines and connecting valves and testing steam guages. A not unimportant feature, too, with Mr. Thurston is repair work of all kinds.

In a word, he is thoroughly competent and reliable in all that he does.

J. M. CALLAHAN.

The Popular Agent of the Chicago and Northwestern Railway.

There is probably not a better known or more popular young business man in the Twin cities than J. M. Callahan, the Chicago and Northwestern Railway company's representative at this point. Mr. Callahan was born in Menasha June 13, 1862, and has been in the employ of this company almost continuously since he left school at Appleton. He was a telegraph operator for many years, reiving his present appointment in 1893. Mr. Callahan is popular with all who knew him. He was appointed postmaster at Neenah under the Cleveland administration but declined, preferring to remain with his first love—the Northwestern.

W. C. JACOBS & SON.

One of the Most Progressive Grocery Firms in the City of Neenah.

This well known establishment, which is located at 303 Commecial street, was established by W. C. Jacobs in 1882, and by him was successful carried on alone until 1890 when his son Thomas L. became a partner and the firm title changed to W. C. Jacobs & son, which title remains the same, although the senior member, W. C. Jacobs, is now deceased. The concern does a very large local retail trade, and as they buy for spot cash and sell on the same basis, patrons are always assured the very best the market affords at the lowest possible prices. Their stock throughout is invariably found fresh, clean, inviting and appetizing. Prompt and accurate delivery to any part of the twin cities.

DEFNET & JENSEN.

Well-Known as Reliable Dealers in Wood and Coal.

For the last two and one-half years Defnet & Jensen have conducted a successful wood and coal business in this city, dealing in superior grades of hard and soft coal and the best qualities of wood, making a specialty of split maple and the carrying of a large stock of kindling wood the year round. The firm, which is composed of Eli Defnet and Jens P. Jensen, also carry lime, sand, cement, cut stone, common brick, fire clay, etc. and are most courteous and accommodating to patrons.

GEO. A. WHITING.

One of the First Paper Manufacturers in the Northwest.

The business career of Geo. A. Whiting, from the time he came to Neenah at about the close of the civil war, when a boy of 16, and how by degrees he has become one of the most extensive manufacturers of paper in the northwest, reads like a romance, and as this is a fitting time to tell the story, The News presumes to publish it, not in a laudatory manner, but simply to illustrate the advantages of any young man who possesses even an ordinary business judgment and has the stamina to carry out his ideas.

Mr. Whiting was born in the old Empire State in 1849, and came to Wisconsin with his parents in 1854, settling at Ripon, where the boy grew up in a manner not unlike most boys. But at the early age of 16 he decided to do something for himself. His parents were averse to his leaving home, but being even at that age possessed of the same indomitable courage and self reliance that has been so characteristic of the man throughout his life, he ran away, with a very limited capital. Indeed it is told of him that when he stepped off the train in this city in 1865 his sole worldly possessians amounted to 10 cents. Nothing daunted, however, the young man sought and obtained employment as a clerk in the store of Pettibone & Jones. He was attentive to business, faithful to his employers, capable, honest and frugal, and shortly after he had attained his majority had become the possessor of sufficient funds to embark in business for himself. Mr. Whiting had become a close student of paper-making, and foreseeing the great possibilities thereof decided to embark in the industry. In 1872 we find him one of the original organizers and stockholders in what is now the Kimberly & Clark Co. He did not remain a member of the concern long, however, and in 1875 purchased an interest in the Winnebago Paper Mills. In 1881 he disposed of his stock in the Winnebago, and in partnership with Wm. Gilbert erected the Gilbert & Whiting mills. Five years later he bought Mr. Gilbert's interests and has since operated the plant alone. His mills to-day are among the most modern in this section, having been entirely rebuilt after the fire of 1888. He manufactures fine machine finished and super calandered books, calendered writings and French folios, and the plant is taxed to its utmost capacity to supply the demand.

In 1888 Mr. Whiting organized the Centralia Pulp and Water Power Co., and, disposing of his interests therein, three years later purchased valuable water powers along the Wisconsin river, after which he built the Wisconsin River Paper & Pulp Co. plant at Whiting, two miles south of Stevens Point, of which immense industry he has ever since been president and principal stockholder. This concern possesses one of the finest water powers in the United States and manufactures 80,000 pounds of pulp per day and produces a like number of pounds of print paper every twenty-four hours. A year later, 1893, Mr. Whiting organized the Plover Paper Co. at the same point. This mill is one of the finest, if not the very best, in its class in the United States. They manufacture high grade writing paper, extra fine halftone papers, and super calandered book papers, the capacity being 40,000 pounds per day.

To give some idea of the immensity of the three mills, of which Mr. Whiting is the practical head, it is but necessary to state that a total of 450 to 500 people are constantly employed therein and that the product of the combined plants are considerably more than $1,000,000 per year. Mr. Whiting is an important factor in the paper-making world to-day, and that an attained his position solely upon his own efforts is all the more creditable

Aside from the paper industry, Mr. Whiting has been an active man in many other directions. He has extensive interests in valuable unimproved water powers, as well as a number of other important investments. He was one of the organizers of the First National bank of our sister city, and in '93 assisted in founding the Citizens National bank at Stevens Point, in which sound financial institution he is still a heavy stockholder. In a word, Geo. A. Whiting has had a most remarkably successful career, never having been connected with a single venture that proved unprofitable whether he remained therewith or not, which clearly denotes that he is a man gifted with unusual faculties for fore telling the outcome of investment.

Mr. Whiting has never aspired to political preferment, respectfully but most emphatically declining all tenders in that direction. In earlier years, however, he was induced to become an alderman and it was '84-'85 served at the head of the municipal government. He is a firm believer, however, in the policy of the Republican party and never fails to do his duty to advance the interests thereof. He was appointed colonel on the staff of Gov. Schofield in '97 and accepted the honor with ease and grace. Mr. Whiting is very prominent in fraternal work, especially Masonry, of which order he has been a member for many years, having been master of Kane Lodge for six years. He is a 32 degree mason and a Shriner and takes an active interest in the welfare of the order.

Mr. Whiting occupies a magnificent home on Forest avenue, a fine half-tone cut which appears elsewhere in this issue of The News. The house, which stands in a beautiful grove on a portion of the land formerly occupied by the old Gov. Doty mansion, is constructed chiefly of handsome monolith red sand stone, the stone used in the building being the celebrated monolith taken from the Prentice quary near Bayfield. This was the largest single stone ever quarried in the United States, being 150 feet long and 10 feet square at base and 4x10 feet at the top, and weighing something like 1,500,000 pounds It was offered to the World's Columbian Exposition as well as to the city of Milwaukee, but was found to be too heavy to move in one piece. So Mr. Whiting purchased it and had it converted into building material for his new home, which is said to be one of the finest and costliest in this section. The home is certainly a substantial affair, and does credit not only to Mr. Whiting but to Neenah as well.

Mr. Whiting has an accomplished wife, whom he married in 1870. She was Miss Edna F. Babcock, daughter of Rev O. W. Babcock. She is a highly cultured lady, and has gained much praise from connoisseurs as an artist of undoubted ability. Every painting in the Whiting home is from the brush of Mrs. Whiting One son, master Frank, aged 14, a most promising child, rounds out the pleasures of home life for Mr. and Mrs. Whiting.

J. J. LEUTENEGGER.

An Extensive Dealer in Minneapolis Flour, Feed, Groceries, Provisions, Etc.

An example of what industry and frugality, coupled with a clever conception of how one shall accomplish for a man of determination, is shown in the case of J. J. Leutenegger who began business in this city in a small an unpretentious manner in 1880 and to-day is an extensive wholesaler and retailer. For ten years he...

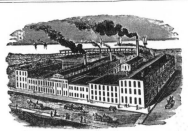

NEENAH STOVE WORKS.
BERGSTROM BROS. & CO.

BERGSTROM BROS. & CO.

Manufacturers of a Full Line of Stoves, Ranges, Furnaces, Etc.

This is one of the oldest and most important manufacturing industries in the Fox River Valley, having been established in this city in 1857 by W. N. and A. K. Moore, and B. W. Wells under the firm title of Moore & Wells. Several years later the Moore brothers purchased Mr. Wells' interest. In 1870 W. N. Moore retired from the firm and the business was carried on by A. K. Moore until his death in 1873. The concern then passed into the hands of Smith, Van Ostrand & Leavens, who operated it until 1878, at which time it was purchased by D. W. and Geo. O. Bergstrom and H. Babcock, the firm being titled Bergstrom Bros. & Co.

From the moment this firm acquired the property until the present day improvement and progression has been the order of the day. The firm manufactures a complete line of wrought steel ranges, cook and heating stoves, furnaces, etc., and their product finds ready sale throughout the United States, their entire line presenting to the dealer everything that is new and desirable in the manufacture of such goods. As is well-known to the trade, there are not more perfect or honest goods on the market than this company's line of "Royal" stoves and ranges. They are perfect in build and possess many new and desirable features not contained in other makes.

The plant occupied by Bergstrom Bros. & Co. is an unusually large one, being complete in every detail as a model in modern stove-making.

C. W. NELSON.

Expert in Sanitary Plumbing and Steam and Hot Water Heating.

For the past five years or more, or to be correct, since January 15, 1894, C. W. Nelson has been in the plumbing business in this city on his own account, and as an instance of the success he is meeting with it is but necessary to state that he gives steady employment to a number of skilled workmen, the number often being 20. Mr. Nelson learned the plumbing trade with George W. Spence, of Milwaukee, He makes a specialty of sanitary plumbing, steam and hot water heating, bath room outfits, sewer work etc., and has done much of the important work in this line hereabouts ever since he has been in business. His place is at 122 East Wisconsin avenue, where he carries a complete line of plumbers' supplies.

MERRITT L. CAMPBELL.

Prominent as a Lawyer—An Exceedingly Busy Man.

There is probably not a business man in the city of Neenah whose time is more constantly occupied than that of Merritt L. Campbell, the well-known lawyer. Aside from an exceptionally large practice, especially in cases involving heavy interests, Mr. Campbell's time is devoted to building up the Equitable Fraternal Union, of which order he is supreme secretary. As is well known, this fraternal organization had its inception in Neenah, and during the two years it has been in existence has attained a comparatively remarkable membership Mr. Campbell was one of the prime movers in organizing the Union, and its success is not a little due to his faithful attention to all matters pertaining thereto. The gentleman is also secretary of the Twin City Building-loan and Savings Association.

M. L. Campbell is a native of this section of the State, and for the last 10 years has made his permanent residence in Neenah. He is recognized as one of the city's most progressive men, one who never allows an opportunity of promoting Neenah's best interests to pass.

DAILY NEWS

HENRY VOGT.

Cigar Manufacturer and Dealer in Confectionery, Fruit. Etc.

Mr. Vogt has been a well-known manufacturer of cigars in this city for the past five years, and the product of his factory, where steady employment is given several experienced workmen, finds ready sale throughout the Twin cities and surrounding country. His best-known 10-cent brand is the "Margarita," while his most popular 5-cent goods are "Menu," "Red Wing" and "Riverside." Mr. Vogt, about a year ago, added a full line of confectionery, fruits etc., and now carries these goods as well as smokers' supplies in general His store is located at 115 Commercial street. He has been a resident of Wisconsin about 25 years, and of Neenah for the past seven years.

JOHNSON BROS., MACHINE CO.

Manufacturers of Engines and Mill Machinery, Etc.

One of the oldest machine shops in this part of the country is that of the above concern, which was established by I E. Johnson, the senior member of the present company, about 22 years ago. The Johnson Bros. Machine Co. have a most complete plant, and aside from doing a large business in the manufacture of engines and mill machinery of every description, make regrinding deckle straps for paper machines a specialty. They also do all kinds of repair work and are heavy dealers in steam pipe and fittings. Their plant is a substantial brick, 40x70 feet, and contains all the modern machinery necessary to keep pace with the times.

MERRITT L. CAMPBELL.

aside from an unusually large grocery trade, carries a great stock of the famous Washburn-Crosby "Gold Medal" flour, for which he is the sole local agent, and the Consolidated Co.'s "Ceresota," than which nothing better is produced in the great flour district of Minneapolis. He also deals largely in provisions and feed, dairy salt, lump salt, baled hay, oiled meal, cotton seed meal, corn, oats, seeds, land plaster, etc., and of late has materially increased his capacity for buying grain of all kinds, for which he pays the highest market price. His elevator and warehouse are admirably located in close proximity to railroad tracks, a material advantage in making shipments.

He is a native of Wisconsin, having been born in Washington county in 1854. Having never aspired to public office, respectfully declining whenever tendered, preferring to give his entire time and energy to building up his business, is one of the main reasons why he is to-day the possessor of a large and growing trade and a happy home.

THE UNION HOUSE.

An Exceptionally Good Hotel at the Modest Price of $1 a Day.

The Union House is one of the favored hostelries of Neenah, being located in the very center of the business portion of the city. Since February of the present year it has been operated by J. Romer, who has been a well-known resident of Neenah for the past 13 years. The house is a two story frame, has 24 well-furnished, cleanly and well-kept sleeping rooms, and the table is always such as would please anyone. In a word, it is an inviting home-like place, and Mr. Romer and his assistants strive in every manner possible to make guests comfortable, the house is enjoying a splendid trade. Nothing is left undone. Rates to transients $1 a day. Special rates by the week or month. Stable connections for 50 horses.

FRANK A. LEAVENS.

Agent for Paper Makers' Supplies and Dealer in Coal and Wood.

Frank A Leavens is known as one of Neenah's most enterprising young business men. In 1895 he established the business of manufacturers' and importers' agent for paper makers' supplies, such as felts, jackets, dryer canvas, wires, belting, belt hooks, aniline colors, ultra marine blue, aqramine, soda ash, bleach, clay, flour and twine, hose and packing, etc., in which he transacts a large trade throughout this section.

Mr. Leavens also conducts an extensive coal and wood business, handling all kinds of hard and soft coal and wood, making specialty of Scranton coal, of which there is no better coal in or out of the earth. The premises occupied by Mr. Leavens' office and yards cover about an acre in this coal shed having a capacity for about 600 tons.

HON. S. A. COOK.

S. A. COOK M'F'G. CO.

An Industry of Marked Importance to the Community.

As is well-known, we have a number of large and important manufacturing concerns in our midst, one of the centers of paper making in this country, and it is due to the fact that these large industries are controlled by men of the keenest foresight and the ripest business experience that our people are continually enjoying the pleasures of prosperity. Few are idle in this community who are able to work and desire employment, and in consequence we are a happy, contented people.

One of the concerns that has done its share in helping to bring about this pleasing condition of things in the S. A. Cook Manufacturing Co., which was organized in the fall of 1897. The plant is that formerly occupied by the Paul Paper Co. The Cook Co. remodelled it and converted a part thereof into a shingle mill. The company manufactures hoods, manilla and print paper and paper specialties, as well as Wisconsin and Michigan white; cedar shingles and fence posts, and gives steady employment to a force of about 100 persons. Their product is known for its uniform reliability, and therefore finds ready sale wherever offered.

S. A. Cook, the head of the company, is one of Neenah's most representative men; indeed, he is a man known throughout the northwest in general and Wisconsin in particular, and whenever he can be induced to temporarily release the ties of business he is sought to accept some high office. Mr. Cook has been honored with the mayoralty of Neenah, a seat in the assembly, an election to the 54th congress by a marked majority of preference, and in the last United States senatorial contest in this State came within a narrow margin of being chosen to that high and honored position. He has time and again been tendered office, and although he can always find opportunity to give of his time, energy and money in the general interests of Republicanism, it is rare he will accept any tender looking to his own advancement in this direction. The Hon. S. A. Cook is truly a man of the people, one who hesitates not in going out among his factory workers and extending the honest hand of fellowship to the humblest among them. There are few if any who know Samuel A. Cook but who admire his many qualities of head and heart. He is essentially a self-made man, having came to this state from Ontario in 1856, when a mere lad. He served in the civil war under Gen. Custer, and was mustered out at the close with honor and distinction to his credit. He resumed farming and in the early '70's, having saved up a few hundred dollars, through the practice of the strictest economy and frugality, and went into business on his own book, opening a small general store at Unity, Marathon county. He prospered, not only in a mechanical way, but as well in the deep permanent residence in Neenah in 1881 he was possessed of a fairly goodly amount of this world's goods—all owing to his honesty of purpose, indefatigable perseverance and inmate business ability. He is indeed a man among men, and his career through life is such as both he and his posterity can point to with pride.